DATE		

Tamara

Tamara

Eeva Kilpi

Translated from the Finnish by
Philip Binham

A Merloyd Lawrence Book
DELACORTE PRESS / SEYMOUR LAWRENCE

A *Merloyd Lawrence Book*
Published by
Delacorte Press/Seymour Lawrence
1 Dag Hammarskjold Plaza
New York, New York 10017

Originally published in Finnish by
Werner Söderström Osakeyhtiö, Helsinki
Copyright © 1972 by Eeva Kilpi

Manufactured in the United States of America
First U.S.A. printing

Library of Congress Cataloging in Publication Data
Kilpi, Eeva.
Tamara.

"A Merloyd Lawrence book."
I. Title.
PZ4.K48325Tam [PH355.K518]   894'.541'33
ISBN 0-440-08494-6   77-18751

Tamara

T amara is going out. She undresses, throwing garments
around the room—or perhaps she is already dressing.
Thin pantyhose hung over the back of a chair stir as
she dashes back and forth past them. Maybe they're what
she's looking for. Compared with stockings, they have the
advantage that they can both be found together.

I can still remember the fellow who got her to change to
pantyhose. The man had fingered her garters in surprise,
stretched them, laughing softly. He'd been much younger
than Tamara and had never seen stockings and garters, except
his mother's. Tamara had defended them vehemently, spoken
of romance and symbolism, the precious erotic tradition
attached to them that will be lost when they go. But deep
inside herself she was ashamed, she admitted, and began to
hate garters from then on. Perhaps this incident was in fact
the reason why their affair ended quickly, though its beginning was so promising and Tamara was so enthusiastic at
first, as usual. Strange how some men succeed in making

1

themselves memorable. I have not asked whether she re- members him still, and to what extent. She's always doing something else when I remember. True, I've had some prob- lems because of this very dual piece of clothing. Nonetheless, it has made our lives easier. So in this matter I feel grateful on the whole; people affect one another's lives to an incal- culable extent.

"Blow," says Tamara, and lifts her foot in front of my face. She has painted her toenails red and the varnish is not drying quickly enough. I grasp her ankle and begin to blow. I turn her ankle and spread her toes apart. She drops down in the armchair beside me, swinging her other foot. She has beautiful feet, though a little short. The toes press touchingly against each other; spreading them apart seems very intimate. When toes atrophy entirely one day, the human race will be one erogenous area the poorer. Already it has virtually lost the capacity to grasp with its lower extremities, not to speak of more sensitive contact.

I catch her other foot in my hand and pull them both right into my lap. She sinks on her back into the chair and I blow so hard that the decrease of oxygen in my blood suddenly makes me feel dizzy. I don't mind: on the contrary, I like intense experiences. They keep depression away.

"I have to hurry," she says.

"I know. They'll soon be dry. They hardly stick now."

She paints only her toenails. Fortunately. If I had to blow on her fingers as well, I'd faint. Not that I personally have anything against fainting, but it would be unnecessarily dramatic, especially since Tamara is so used to all kinds of things. It would be wasted on her. And would only delay her.

On a rainy evening like this, and particularly when she is late, she takes a cab, though she is usually careful about money and always begrudges the fare. I imagine that her fingers tremble involuntarily as she raises the receiver and begins to dial the number.

While waiting for the cab, she pulls the belt of her rain-

2

coat tight and turns her back as she ties a scarf around her head. In the days when she still wore stockings, I had to check that the seams were straight. Odd my remembering things like that now.

"I mature slowly," she has a habit of saying of herself. "I graduated to short skirts when other people were wearing them calf-length again. I don't like to do anything until I'm quite ready for it." All the same, she said recently: "At the decisive moment one must be prepared to go beyond one's unpreparedness. A new step is always for a moment a step into air."

"There's some cucumber in the fridge, I got it on the way," she says, standing in front of the mirror. "I could get you something from the café, the taxi will wait."

"We've only just finished eating."

"But if you want something . . ."

"I don't want . . ." I say, and catch her eye in the mirror, "anything really."

And for a moment I am infuriated. In all these years I have not learned a simple thing like controlling my voice. It breaks even at moments when I am otherwise completely controlled, moments that are familiar and commonplace, like this one. All of a sudden, to my own surprise, there's a peculiar little crack in my voice, as if in answer to the almost invisible trembling of Tamara's fingers; as if, independent of ourselves, our bodies might speak a sign language to one another, caress each other tenderly without either of us knowing, and shyly declare a longing that seems much too solemn to put into words on an ordinary evening. I don't want her to imagine that I'm sad, because I'm not. She would be surprised if she knew my thoughts about pantyhose and seams, but I don't wish to upset her mood by reminding her of the past. Or, who knows, perhaps she is remembering the same things herself. I must find out on some appropriate occasion.

"I won't be late," she says, "or else I won't be back till

3

morning. In any case I'll pass this way, so don't worry. And I can manage perfectly well without breakfast, in fact it's good for me now and then."

I can't stand that sort of thing. Starting to chatter just when she's going out the door. At one time she used to embrace me and kiss me just before she went out. She'd even nip my ear or ruffle my hair. I could put up with that even less. When I finally revealed my feelings to wean her of this habit, she appeared to be sincerely sorry. But I was merciless. After all, I have some rights. Yes, sometime I must speak to her about this habit of talking nonsense in the last three minutes.

I listen attentively to her footsteps on the stairs as if it were my duty; then I move to the window and watch her run through the drizzling rain, raincoat shiny under the street-lamp, to the waiting taxi, and bend to get in. I briefly see her feet, pale against the sidewalk, in their little shoes. Then she draws them in, slams the door, and the cab goes off, leaving me behind as if I were the past tense.

The long flowers of the aspen fall on the asphalt. That's the first real sign of spring in these parts even when it is cold, windy, and rainy as this spring has been; mere waiting. Aspen flowers are first red and bloated, as if ready to burst; then they stretch out and finally dangle in the slightest breeze like the dull, too long hair of some old creature and float down in the end almost lighter than air, reluctantly. Now the rain helps them. They fall heavy as grubworms and remain coiled on the asphalt, gradually covering the road. Against the giant, shaggy background of the old tree, the young flowerless aspens are like the stiff, classical, silvery embroidery on a linen tablecloth I remember from my childhood.

I no longer ask Tamara who she is meeting. She tells me without asking. I can hardly wait for her return.

However, after winding my watch and drawing down the blinds (in town I prefer to sleep in the dark), I decide to work for a couple of hours. Actually, this is my best time.

4

Everything is quiet. Only the muffled noise of a car or someone whistling for his dog can be heard, but these sounds don't worry me. This is a secluded street, undisturbed by traffic. I take down my file and newspaper clippings. I'd like to put them all in order for once, but that would take weeks. I'll do it some day when I am no longer good for anything, even in this line. Tamara threatens to clean out the closets at the same time. How dreadful this house will be when everything is finally neat and we sit amid files all numbered and in alphabetical order and hygienic cupboards.

I worked for two hours, and efficiently, in my opinion. The psychology of language hasn't been studied much in our country, and source books are scanty; many of them are superficial popular works used as lower-level textbooks. One must go forward alone and trust to bold associations, intuition, and creativity. In any case I couldn't work in any other way. If only I could succeed in giving some slight impetus to the scientific study of the correspondence between idea and expression, or could incite some young scholar to prepare a new statistical comparison of word frequencies in various languages; I am thinking chiefly, of course, of the vocabulary connected with emotional and sexual life, in its precise terminology and in the inadequacies of everyday speech . . . but maybe I am aiming too high. However, it's a problem that preoccupies me. We have not yet fully recognized the significance of language as a means of expressing the creative powers of this species. We may well be the only animal that narrates.

I had been sleeping for some time when Tamara returned. Through a gap in the blinds I saw that dawn had not yet broken. She'd come back early and spring nights are short. The first birds were chirping sleepily, as if to wake one another.

She pushed her hand under the covers and felt me. I pretended to be asleep. She tapped my ribs as if she were playing them. Someone whom she had once liked had said "ribs are a lovely instrument," and since then she often repeated this movement. I don't know whether she still remembered this or whether in general she remembers half the things I do. She kicks up one here, one there, and only I, her memory, still remember where they came from. I turned on my side and she snuggled against me.

"Are you asleep?"

I put my arm around her and drew her closer.

"That man had long underpants on when I got there," Tamara said. "Can you imagine, he came down to the street door to let me in wearing a ragged old bathrobe and these baggy underpants. And we hadn't met for ages. And he started getting undressed right away."

I pictured her standing in the unfamiliar hall, green scarf on her head, painted toenails peeping through her thin stockings at the tip of her open shoes, an expression of surprise and restrained disappointment on her face.

"In the hall?"

"Yes. He took off that ghastly bathrobe and hung it on a nail in the hall cupboard, but then under that were those brown underpants and an old-fashioned undervest, you know, one of those with holes."

"I know, I've never been able to stand them," I said proudly. "What did he do then?"

"Then he kissed me."

"And you?"

"I shut my eyes and put my arms around his neck. I'd been almost missing him and I was afraid he wouldn't call me anymore."

"And then?"

"Then he went into his room, took off the rest of his clothes, and lay down on the bed. For a moment I thought of leaving right away; he often annoys me with his ways. But anyway I didn't go. Besides, I thought how disappointed he'd be. So I took my coat off and hung it up. Then I went into his room and took my other clothes off. I folded them

6

carefully on the back of a chair," she said, as if to please me, and I thought for a moment of the clothes thrown in all directions that I had picked up just a few hours ago from all sorts of unlikely places and positions in this room.

"Then?"

Tamara didn't reply.

I pressed her close to me. Her hair was long and hung loose over her shoulders. I was tangled in it. I began to mold her body, to create it for myself, to bring it back to my mind and my fingertips' memory. It acknowledged me and greeted me weakly, like a tired relative back from a journey. And I gathered her gradually into my arms, so that at length she was in my embrace like a basket of fruit, of new potatoes, of fragrant steaming beets; food of my desire that I gorged on without ever having my fill—"As if increase of appetite had grown/By what it fed on" touched my thoughts like a message from a bygone generation, from men greater than I, who have struggled as hard.

"Did you get any pleasure from it?" I asked.

She nodded into my armpit.

"Oh yes, he's good in bed, only he always wants to do everything with his fingers, and you should know that's not enough for me."

Yes, I did know that. And I was overwhelmed with an immense desire to kiss her all over, to be kind to her, to reward her. And I asked her to tell me more, to describe details and stages. I demanded nuances that she had not thought of mentioning or considered insignificant, although I had many times besought her to remember them particularly. But she had a poor memory, she was lazy and absent-minded, tired and past the actual event, so that I had to coax and surmise, make my own suggestions and put forward alternatives before the total picture evolved and I was convinced that she had had her moment of happiness and that this man, in spite of what one might call his absurdity, had succeeded in satisfying her. For such was evidently—

7

oddly enough—the case. And only when I was convinced of this did my inner tension relax, and I sank against Tamara soaked from head to foot, exhausted, the sweat dripping onto her face, wetting her neck and hair.

It is strange that in this situation I often think about the possibility of our separating, each going our own way, not meeting again; nothing more needed in our case. I used to mention this to Tamara, first as a kind of trial, then to hear her denial. Perhaps in this state of mind I once really thought I could do that, at least that.

But she decisively rejected my thought each time.

"I can't stand being alone," she said. "And I want to be free. You understand my conditions, I yours. That's a lot, more than usual."

Over the years she has given many other explanations, like the vague "love is the only thing worth living for" and the linguistically dubious "I'm allergic to the idea of being rejected, I can't take it, I must have someone who doesn't run away." And so on.

True, I don't run away.

"Are you going to meet him again?"

"I hope so," she said, half asleep. "He never promises anything. And I never ask."

It seems that people like Tamara very much, but actually she has no friends. Rather she is the friend of many, quite a different matter. Is a person's friend ever, in the end, the one he puts his trust in? Is not friendship always too airy and independent to permit this, and should not its characteristic nearness be protected from the burden of trust, which a stranger can more easily bear? That's how it is, I imagine, in marriage. It's unreasonable to demand from such a close relationship, already burdened with the intimacy both of sex and of a mutual economy (in itself a combination approaching the bounds of human endurance), that it should also include trust, the sharing of moods and of secrets, all that goes under the name of "honesty." For this is to deprive man of his last private domain, the path to his own hidden springs. No wonder people wilt like plants whose roots have been gnawed by moles.

I don't mean to compare our relationship to marriage, or to say that Tamara feels her friendlessness is a deficiency. I only consider these things in passing, and it cannot be denied that they come to mind easily as means of comparison against which to measure the most varying human relations. I wouldn't even call our relationship confidential. It is something much too fundamental to be described by such a furtive word. We're like two funnels, one inside the other; all that Tamara experiences flows to me. Or my life could be called an essay—that neglected, intellectualized literary form —entitled "Tamara," strange though that may seem considering her sensuality and way of living.

These were my thoughts the following evening, while I was eating green pepper and cheese—when I'm alone I don't bother to stuff the cheese into the pepper; I always have some surprising tidbit in case she should come.

It's true that every now and then I worry about her, though I'm no longer afraid as I was years ago. I no longer fear that her many affairs might hurt her, because I know that she listens to the voice of her emotions and follows it absolutely. Anyone who does that stays pure. I am worried that her capacity to be disappointed, of which she is so proud, will one day disappoint her in some way for which she is not prepared, or that her measure will be filled so tragically that she won't be able to go on. Say what you will, people have their breaking point; after they've reached it they are either shattered or petrified. The most shallow never reach it, the most tenacious manage to delay it, and the most sensitive hang on to it all their lives as to a reed amid the waves, solving their problems with suffering, and showing immense talent for it and immense strength. They are even able to sink devotedly, in an ecstasy of will, strength, and suffering.

9

During the past winter I was often overwhelmed by the feeling that our relationship was changing, that some crisis awaited it. They say that in marriage too—again the comparison—there are phases, special seasons when the relationship is in a danger zone or balanced or changing its essential nature. True, I can't point to any clear signs of this; it's only a feeling, perhaps a fancy. I may have been afraid of the idea from the beginning and rejected it, but now it begins—as do all rejected things before long—to penetrate the consciousness. Yet I feel that something in Tamara calls forth this fancy; moreover, she has often said that she is seeking a permanent relationship with someone, someone she'd never want to leave. On the other hand, I doubt whether she's been quite as frank recently as before. Several times it seemed that she was hiding something, keeping important things to herself, perhaps making things up. She would have no trouble fabricating any stories she liked, with such a wealth of material at her disposal.

Of course it may be that I am imagining—my aloneness, my disability, gives birth to these thoughts. There are scientists who claim that a physical defect always develops its spiritual counterpart. Others maintain that it gives rise to compensation, development of contiguous abilities which one can then concentrate on, choose from. I am inclined to believe both theories. Once I saw a young man bouncing gaily along on crutches and one leg, the other trouser leg turned up and fastened with safety pins, and I couldn't help thinking that the leg had just been amputated. He walked in the way and at the speed of someone with two legs. One-leggedness had not yet marked him. After he'd adapted he would move differently, perhaps more skillfully, but his mind would be oppressed by his disability.

I never understood those doctors who want a person to accept his illness. That's the greatest self-deception there can be. I'll never accept my own. It's an affliction for me and always will be. There is nothing I can do about it. I curse it with open eyes, without pretending that it is good this way. It burdens my existence every moment. Only Tamara can rouse in me feelings that break the general tone of my life. And often, it cannot be denied, my work also has that effect, this research mostly ignored by a society interested in more recent, more destructive branches of science. Life is what it feels like. At my age I can safely say so.

Sometimes it annoys me that I did not keep a journal of Tamara's liaisons as well as of her own accounts of them from the beginning. In that way I'd have been able to confirm my idea that there has been a steady development of her relationships over the years, and that the trend right from the start has been toward continuity. Recently she admitted this herself several times, as if in passing or accidentally. This is noteworthy, for previously she'd vehemently denied the need for a permanent human relationship. When we first became acquainted, she considered it sufficient for a person to have work and a sex life. Separate from one another. The next step was that she began to say how wonderful the combination of the two was. That's a real stroke of luck, she said. And true enough she did have at that time a pretty successful affair which combined the two. At a mental hygiene congress in Götenberg she had met a Catholic social worker, who was called Father Andres because he looked like a priest; for six months they had together compiled statistics about vagrancy in southern Finnish towns and built up some sort of emergency aid plan of which a few small details were, as I recall, even carried out. Father Andres had later moved to Denmark and lived, I believe, in some kind of commune, where Tamara was welcome to go if she got too fed up with the madmen in her own country. During that six months she did seem pretty content, although the ending of the affair, because of Father Andres's calling, appeared to affect her deeply. "But I've been trained for just that sort of thing," she said. "Life has purposely taught me to specialize in the ending of loves ever since I lost my first love because of the

11

war. After that I couldn't understand for a long time that people might voluntarily reject each other, and that other things besides bombs and death separate people. That discovery later on was really traumatic."

I am the last phase in Tamara's life representing continuity for her, the one to whom she can always return after work and sex, who remains within reach, does not run away, does not reject. "You're vital to me" she has sometimes said casually when she was getting ready to go out, concentrating all her attention on not tripping on her pantyhose as she pulls them on, sitting on the edge of my bed in postures that are eternal, only the clothing varying a little, if the artists can be believed. I follow this preparation earnestly as ever, because it pleases me and seems to mean something to her too. Besides, I too have my weak moments when I beg for recognition, though I consider this degrading and find it usually does more harm than good to both parties.

For years it seemed that the combination of work, sex, and continuity—each neatly cared for in its own sector—gave her adequate satisfaction and security. And for me, as is no doubt apparent, these years meant fulfillment and surprises such as I never have expected from life, or believed would come my way. I am filled not only with love but with deep gratitude as well.

And yet it seems increasingly clear that over the years I've only become the inevitable fixed point from which Tamara can safely seek her real life. She believes that this life awaits her somewhere, untouched, and that fate owes her this because of all the injustices of the past. "Life can't have intended to disappoint a woman like me," she says, "to leave her alone, to make her suffer and wait. It's a mistake. Or it's wrong, a wrong that must be righted while I'm still alive. I've made my complaint to life and I'm waiting for the error to be mended."

And when I look at her, I believe she is right: life can't have meant her to suffer and be disappointed. She is so clearly made to be loved. Like every one of us. There has been some terrible misunderstanding, a universal bad judgment. And it still affects us all.

And Tamara has decided to set right this mistake, this greatest stupidity of mankind. She's gone trumpeting to war, and at the very last moment, as she says dramatically.

I almost feel the need to defend her, and I do defend her. At the same time painfully admitting that in spite of all the continuity that I have meant to her and wished to mean, she still feels lonely and without love. The need for love is only fulfilled if, besides being loved, one loves in return. An impossible demand in fact, because of the extreme complexity of this apparently simple situation, especially when we consider man's lamentable incapacity in this field.

In her concrete defense, it must be said that I have, because of my illness, been impotent all the time we've known each other. Or rather that my illness, after its clinical symptoms had been cured, left behind, along with other things, this reminder of itself. It means in practice that the only satisfaction I can get comes through my imagination. I've been lucky to find a woman willing to go along, to open her innermost soul, the pastures of her mind to me. And I must admit that for my part I am not easily satisfied. On the contrary, I've always demanded more and more, ever more unqualified abandon. Variety, sense of reality, good taste, and imagination. If I add morality to this, my catalogue of demands is just about complete; I cannot abide licentiousness or debauchery; a filthy combination of insensibility and sensuality repels me as much as the exploitation of natural forces.

So for me life could stop here. I desire no more, I believe no longer in miracles (except when I forget that I've lost this belief), not even happy accidents which until recently encouraged my optimism. But for Tamara matters are still midway. As far as I've been able to judge from her development up to now, her spirit—or rather her subconscious—

strives toward unity, a coming together of the separate tracks between which her life is now divided. She longs for a fundamental unity in her life, or her identity, to use the fashionable terminology. But that is far too narrow and static a concept for a process that involves the integration of her self, the meeting of love, sex, and continuity, this dream of fundamental security characteristic of adulthood—even if it remains a dream. I would not grudge it her, though I know it would mean the end of our relationship, end of this rare, unique, highly moral, mutually respectful human contact.

We have often observed that we could not have managed without each other. Or that we would have managed considerably worse, suffering and pining. And I have also wondered, forgetting my work for hours at a time, whether there is anything essential lacking in us after all. Perhaps people are only fascinated by inessentials like jewelry and stimulants; perhaps they only imagine that they need to have everything.

Then Tamara comes, in the middle of my thought, her skin glowing and smooth like that of a woman who has just been loved, even her hair seeming more alive though it was only hurriedly combed, and at once I feel the desire to come close to her, to hear what she has to tell, to ask for details, to know what it was like.

And I press her close to me, I importune her with my questions, until I am convinced that she has had a good time, that she has enjoyed and is satisfied, and she describes what it feels like, until the excitement within me reaches its climax and abates, and my body relaxes.

Even though I said that I suffer, I could as well say that I am one of those enviable people who have already suffered their full measure; the nerve transmitting pain is dead, and its sensitizing effect is gradually dying down. Only curiosity is left, and Tamara, still a living part of me.

All in all: it is amusing, this life.

There was a time when Tamara massaged my legs for hours every day. Properly speaking, I was fit again by that time. I could already move, mostly with the help of my arms it is true, dragging myself from one piece of furniture to another. I hate crutches, not to mention wheelchairs. Besides, I've always been bored with anything that is programed. I don't believe that two or three hours of physical exercise a day are of any use if one's soul is completely against it. Right from my school days physical education and sports periods were repulsive to me, and I never felt my lack of ability as strongly as when the whole class was bouncing around in immaculate shorts, dashing to the other end of the room to the apparatus—I suppose I should know its name; or when a ball was coming at me with enormous speed (in which case of course I instinctively avoided it), with everybody first shouting "catch it, catch it" and then "butterfingers," "clumsy."

I had charming, patient nurses, to whom I showed my

appreciation by praising their skill in giving enemas; quite often I succeeded in getting an extra one. I do not claim to have been an agreeable patient; on the contrary it may be that my unpleasantness hastened my discharge from the hospital; especially since I promised to wiggle my toes two thousand five hundred times every two hours, twist my ankles in the interim both clockwise and counterclockwise, and press with my whole weight ten to twenty times against the bedboard every single evening as hard as I could. At that time my toes did not move at all, but now and again they'd have involuntary fits of trembling, which was considered an encouraging sign of nerve function. Nowadays I mostly move around under my own power, though it's not very attractive to watch. Out of doors I can lean elegantly on a stick so that, as Tamara says, I resemble a gentleman of the past century who has a rendezvous; in the garden I move around freely, somehow or other.

Tamara never saw me as I was formerly, and I don't think she would have noticed me as I was then. I am probably not her type at all. She herself claims that for a long time she noticed only my legs, and would not even have recognized me if I had met her in the street walking like other people. Of course, she does exaggerate in her own way. She even claims that my legs fascinated her right from the start; she always positioned herself at lectures so that she could see them under my table. And indeed I remember her always at the end of the row halfway down the room, sitting oddly sideways and seeming to crane her neck. I imagined she was trying to look out of the window, but this was evidently not the case. I have no reason to doubt her word since it is rather her habit to be brutally direct. True, I understand that leg fetishism is more characteristic of men than women, but that in itself proves nothing.

For a long time our relationship was only verbal, though this does not at all mean that it was not from the first an intimate one. Her way of speaking, or even of just opening

16

her mouth, aroused erotic fantasies in me. She told me later that she noticed this at once, but at the time she put it down to her own voluptuous state of mind, the result of her current love affair. It is well known that some people in love want to embrace the whole world, to use a well-worn but graphic phrase, and beyond doubt Tamara is one of these. As soon as she falls in love she wants to please all, to share her joy with everyone. Lack of love, on the other hand, makes her avoid people, even those of whom she otherwise approves, "hate the whole human race, that unbearable, low species." Or, even worse, she sinks into an apathy that depresses her for weeks and "makes everything seem empty."

Before long, however, it became clear that we were in fact stirring one another. I was in the habit of inviting my students to my home for their oral examinations, so that the fact that Tamara began to come there was nothing unusual. I made her learn the laws of Hammurabi by heart. I gave her a frequency study to do of some personal form appearing in the Apocrypha, I don't remember which. I dug out from my shelves a dusty history of the martyrs and said that nobody had yet done a study of it from the standpoint of sexual roles, and that we could start to do an outline for it orally. She even put up with that. But when I took out my Herodotus, trying feverishly to think of a difficult psycholinguistic subject on it (something like sexual pathological symptoms in Herodotus in light of sentence rhythms), she suddenly stood up as if she had had enough, came over to stand in front of me, and looked me in the eyes, lips trembling. Because of the weakness in my legs and my slightly hunched stance, she is a little taller than I when standing.

I wouldn't have been surprised if she had slapped my face. I deserved it. My heart ached at the thought that now I was going to lose her.

"May I massage your legs?" she asked.

That same spring she stopped studying psycholinguistics and started on the courses in practical therapy that led her

17

to her present field. Since then she has also studied anthroposociology and social psychology. But she never got her degree, nor in spite of all my requests did she move in with me.

"You would have made a teacher of me," she says. "Who knows where in the backwoods I'd be now, my only joy in asking my male pupils home after giving them such difficult tasks that they couldn't manage by themselves. It was a good thing you were so awful. I had to choose what I am doing now. I have to feel that people depend on me; I'm just the right sort for that."

So in time she dispelled the thought which worried me at first, that perhaps I had influenced the course of her life too much.

Besides, even if I had known that I was doing wrong, I would not have been able to act otherwise when this unbelievable thing appeared within my reach. To tell the truth, had I ever dared imagine that such an opportunity would be offered me, I'd have been prepared, if necessary, to snatch it, to tear it from life. Nor have I the slightest intention of relinquishing my conviction now. All in all, everything happened as it should have. We simply had to be true to ourselves. Nothing would have come of any kind of self-sacrifice. And Tamara understands these things, knows these laws like her ten fingers.

It must be admitted that her taste in men is odd, and surely I am the right person to say so. At the moment she is most interested in someone who, for want of better identification, goes by the name of Checks, because according to Tamara he often wears a jacket with loud checks and a shirt with a different kind of loud checks. This doesn't prove anything more than bad taste. He should not be confused with the man already mentioned, identified mainly by his underwear. For the sake of simplicity we call him the Communist; he is one of the rare radical intellectuals who wear long underpants. At one time I myself thought that they were the same person, since the types of clothing seemed to tally so well, until the actual situation became clear and I was obliged to divide this imaginary man, whom I had dressed up so carefully, in two, one of whom was left only with his eternal underpants, the other with his check jacket and shirt. Unfortunately, misunderstandings and masculine hybridizations like this occur from time to time, no matter how

19

earnestly I strive to keep up to date, since it is most important for me to identify each lover if I am to imagine myself in his place.

"Doesn't he have any other distinguishing characteristics besides these checks?" I asked Tamara.

"No, he's quite ordinary. That's just why he interests me."

"No beard, no long hair, no bitten nails?"

"Nothing like that. Oh yes, he goes to dog shows."

This was dumfounding. How would I manage to identify with him if this should really develop into something? At the very least I'd have to acquire some dog literature: "How I Make My Dog Happy," or "Good, Faithful, Willing." A new man and on top of that quite ordinary, I pondered. Up to now she'd always chosen neurotics. True, in her walk of life she's hardly had other possibilities. All this promised variation in my life, and lonely evenings.

I won't claim that I haven't been disappointed now and then. Maybe I was happy in anticipation of an evening together. I bought wine and something to eat, trying to remember her particular fancies (they too can change unpredictably), and always some sort of surprise—last time it was thin little wafers of rye bread to dip in melted butter. She liked them, as I had guessed she would. One unfailing delicacy is strips of bacon fried so dry and crisp that they crackle between the teeth. These are our secret orgies, and make our lives seem dangerous and wild. "Everyone ought to have a secret life," says Tamara, her lips greasy, sucking her fingertips in the red light of the table lamp, in obvious enjoyment. "Can life in general be anything else than secret, the way the world has gone? People are starting to keep hidden to keep alive like in wartime, they can't manage otherwise."

I agreed as if I were hearing my own voice speaking from some internal cranny. I've often thought what an important thing the human voice is, how poorly off those who have not been granted a beautiful, expressive, sensitive voice that speaks beyond words, how little pleasure is in anything a person says if the tone is wrong, no matter how right.

Then, at moments like this, the telephone will ring.

Or Tamara has already got as far as having a bath, or we are both sitting in the bathtub and I stumble, dripping, to answer it, leaving wet prints everywhere.

"She is having a bath," I say. "Can she call later?"

Yes, she can call and ask for the hotel bar. There is a hellish din in the background.

Tamara will not allow the phone to be disconnected; and when she is here her telephone answering service gives the caller my name. One of her patients or protégés may suddenly need that decisive word that will postpone his suicide awhile. Tamara already saved many lives this way. It may even be true. And I least of all have the right to doubt it. But all the same, sometimes she refuses. I remember how once, at four in the morning, she refused to go somewhere—was it the Konginkangas Summer Festival?—in any case one of those obscure time-consuming occasions that have become such a popular form of escapism, one of the few forms permitted.

When she hears that someone is waiting for her call, Tamara begins to wash herself with great speed. She soaps the brush and asks me to scrub her back—not that I would not do it without being asked, and with pleasure. She has a beautiful long back and strong shoulders; the depressions on each side of her buttocks are like dimples. For many men a woman's back is more exciting than her front, and scientists claim that this stems from our unconscious memories which preserve unknown to us all the past habits of life's evolutionary stages. I do not deny that a woman leaning forward may arouse in a man the desire to jump on her back, to press her buttocks between his palms, to get into her from behind and perhaps even sink his teeth into her neck, below the hairline, or her shoulder blade. As a matter of fact I believe that this possessive bite might help bring success, perhaps be a

21

necessity for it. It is only our morally and erotically impoverished civilization that has begun to interpret it as sadism, which it most certainly was not originally; teeth marks on the shoulder blades greatly raised a woman's self-esteem and made her respected in the eyes of all. For the same reason men have prized scars and inflicted wounds on themselves when they didn't succeed in getting them in war.

After scrubbing her back, which she enjoys so much that she moans, I soap her with my hands, rubbing from above downward, and finally push my finger into her. In this situation it happens so easily that she hardly notices it at first; I have short nails. Although she doesn't enjoy manipulation (so she says), she always permits it in the bath. I carefully wash each fold, and do not hurry. At first she takes no notice, but then begins to pay attention to my finger's movements, until she splashes, moaning, to a sitting position. I take the plug out of the bath and while the water is draining I rub soap on her breasts, her stomach, under her arms, and into her navel. Then, before she has time to recover and change her mind, I take the shower and aim it between her legs. She twists, laughs, and shouts, scolds me and begs for mercy, but I am merciless; I keep the shower in place, and watch the layers of her flesh whipped like the petals of a flower by heavy rain, knowing that I couldn't do this against her will. Finally she strains into an arch, her whole body rigid, eyes blind, drops of sweat on her forehead, and jerks to free herself, yet all the time as if hanging on the shower. Then two, three, four spasms release her and she relaxes in the bath, eyes closed, like a corpse. I rinse her body, armpits, neck, breasts, and when I direct the shower again to the sensitive spot, she is at once shaken by a new, urgent series of spasms. This is the only violence that I ever succeed in doing to her, or rather the only concrete act.

"You devil," she says as she gets out of the bath, winding a towel around her. I can hear that she's not angry, though she is sometimes indignant.

"It makes me as weak as a kitten," she says. "Now I won't be able to do anything."

"What do you need to do?"

She doesn't answer, but only patters her wet feet around the room, dries her ears, looks for something, forgets what she is looking for, doesn't even think to sit down. It gives me secret satisfaction to see her in that state, as if I would take all the credit for it; I know she values such an experience. "Love should take the breath away, make the head spin, erase the sense of time and place, until worlds shatter and carry us into an ultimate liberation." She insists that at the decisive moment, when cars crash into each other, in an earthquake, when someone dies, he feels for a fraction of a second joy because the situation is no longer under his control, that at last he has the right to abandon everything and give up struggling. It is the relief of final surrender, from which he never returns to tell the tale. And in love too, worlds clash together, solar systems explode; but something always remains to wander, and new fusions take place to enrich existence.

All right, I think while she is speaking, all right, here at least I'm as good as the next man.

But I can't help admiring the frenzy of her mind, the dimensions that she conquers. Without them my life would be poorer.

"Who called?" she asks.

"Who on earth was it now?" I say casually, indifferent to the fact that it might be someone already on his way to jump into the Imatra Falls; well, even I'm allowed an occasional irresponsible moment. "I wrote his name down somewhere, I don't remember where—I only remember he was in some hotel bar."

And Tamara goes off with her towel wrapped around her to look for the name and the number. The telephone is on the bedside table, which is covered with scribbled-on bits of paper. While at the phone she is in the habit of drawing strange long-stemmed lilies that seem to be craning with

23

curiosity, or other oddly projecting flowers and long-necked birds. Various kinds of grids or steps are very typical of her, and she often fills the paper starting from the corner with decorative, lacy flourishes reaching in all directions, so that it is practically impossible to find memos, numbers, and messages among them. She also has a habit of writing orders for herself, like "Phone Hans, Aarne, Risto, Mirja. Buy paper clips, carbon paper, four feet of false eyelashes. Take shoes to be mended. Mail forms. Pay membership fee for Sexual Politics Association." Usually, however, she is irritated afterward by her own imperious tone, and I'm left to attend to the tasks listed. The more determined the tone, the more certain it is that I'll have to follow through.

She dials the number, sitting on the edge of the bed with the towel over her shoulders, drops of water swelling at the ends of her hair, dripping to her knees, red-nailed toes curled on the carpet, the tuft of hair between her legs wet and glistening like a sundew. I hear her mention a person's name, unknown to me. While she is waiting for the person to come to the phone, she puts one foot on the bed and dries between her toes. I could watch her all evening like this. Then Tamara explains that she's just had a bath, is still wet, drying her hair will take half an hour, this time won't do at all, absolutely not. I begin to feel happier. The "Lambs' Polka" comes into my mind for some reason and I begin to whistle softly its light-footed beginning.

But then I hear Tamara say: "I do understand how you feel."

And I can imagine the man lying successfully to her at the other end of the line. Nothing is so credible as a good lie. The truth generally sounds outrageous, unbelievable, and always clumsy, except when it is thrown ruthlessly in one's face.

"Will you be much more drunk in an hour's time?" Tamara asks, her voice already willing.

24

I can almost hear him declare that from this very moment he will drink only soda water.

"All right," Tamara says. "I'll be there in an hour's time. Don't get worried if I'm a bit late."

She puts the phone down, takes the hair dryer from the cupboard, and starts to dry her hair. Then she remembers me and begins to explain above the noise: "It's someone I respect, actually I respect him a lot. He says he needs somebody, that he's in the sort of state when he can't call anyone because he won't get any help from them, only get more depressed. And imagine, he said 'in our society,' and he himself is one of the people this society looks to, who ought to be able to help others. I must go and see him."

I had stopped whistling while she was speaking, but the "Lambs' Polka" kept playing in my mind, so that when she finished, its heavy, fateful final bars were just beginning.

"How do you interpret the end of the 'Lambs' Polka,' those gloomy, heavy notes?" I said, and started to hum them.

Tamara turned her head before the dryer and lifted her hair with her hand so that it streamed out as if in a spring wind, on a mountaintop. And I hastened to answer my own question, permitting myself a rare sign of emotion to show her that I was not annoyed at her going.

"Doesn't it describe for you the disappointment that always comes inevitably, the end of love and with it the end of everything, death? The music just gives us the chance of seeing beauty there."

I was sure that for once we would be of the same opinion.

But Tamara looked at me unmoved, turned off the fan, and said: "I've always imagined that it was just the big ram coming, bigger than all the rest."

25

Tamara met the checked man at a charity ball in the winter. People will dance for the benefit of the most outrageous causes, and this tendency must of course be exploited. This time it was a masquerade, which suggests that they did not dare dance in honor of madness quite as themselves, that they were not bold enough to show their faces; or as my mother used to say they "pulled pigskin over their eyes"; the four feet of false eyelashes had gone like hot cakes.

I remember Tamara pulling her black tights on. And a flock of pictures has remained in my mind of her in various attitudes: with knees bent filing her toenails, those eternal demanders of attention; with her left hand raised, her right bent across her breast clipping the hair under her left arm with a small pair of scissors, before I had to come to her help to shear the right side; sitting before the bookshelf with a large encyclopedia on her knee wearing only a black brassiere. Often when she was getting ready we talked about something quite different, argued about some word, until she went to look it up. "Cusp" she reads aloud, "a cusp is . . ." and into my mind glides the idea that a cusp is a naked woman with a book on her knees and about to leave. Painted, this would look artificial, the artist's contrivance to present the human anatomy. But in fact it is a recurring natural pose; who knows what everyday explanation there is for Manet's *Déjeuner sur l'herbe* where a woman sits nude in company with two fully clothed men. Sometimes Tamara remembers right in the middle of everything some certificate that should still be mailed today, and sits there without a stitch on, tapping it out on the typewriter. The name of this picture could be *Air Bath* or *At the Typewriter* or *The Document*. Then she inadvertently walks by a little too near, her rump quivering, and I suddenly lay hold of her.

"I stamp you as my own," I say, kissing wherever I can.

"Your nose is cold, your beard prickles—I'm always ticklish when I'm in a hurry." She twists and turns to get free and pulls my scanty hair. "Let me go."

"I want to taste you first. I'll devour as much as I want. I'll let the rest go where it likes."

She laughs and jerks in my arms. I imagine myself standing up and carrying her struggling to the bed, then throwing myself upon her. She tries to turn away from under me, but I subdue her limb by limb. She presses her legs together, but I separate them with my knees. She tries to pull away, but I cross my hands over her head, so that her face remains between my thumbs. Then I spear her. Tamara has told me that some men grind themselves into a woman as if they were taking a virgin every time. There's no denying that this has its own attraction, Tamara says, especially if it's done gracefully and without hesitation.

"I'd give a lot to be able to rape you," I say.

"That would require resistance on my part," Tamara says. "And it's extremely questionable whether I could manage that."

27

This excitement before the masquerade has remained clearly in my mind, although it is by no means unique in my gallery of images. Perhaps it is the primitive trinity of walking, carrying, and rightful despoiling that makes it so engrossing.

Tamara was dressed in a black, clinging outfit that included a long tail; she was supposed to be a cat. But just when I was about to commend the atmosphere of ruttishness that she had succeeded in creating, she de-eroticized her dress by putting on an old pair of ski boots: puss-in-boots.

The man had brought a bundle on the end of a stick and a spruce sprig in his hat; everything had in fact started long before either of them had suspected anything.

They had danced together and the man had carried out small, unimaginative though successful dance steps, keeping within a safe area, as befits a member of the board, and Tamara had followed obediently. She told me all this much later; neither of us guessed the importance of the event at the time. A woman has to learn a man's steps each time, she said, adapt to a formal or free way of dancing; that's how it always begins.

And suddenly while she was telling me about this she remembered how once, a long time ago, when she was very unhappy, she had danced a wonderful dance. Possibly there were several, one after another, but they seemed to be all one. She had been wearing black lace stockings, the only festive thing about her at the time. The music had been like something from space, unique, not composed, born at that moment and lasting only for that moment; some patients had started a band and they had danced. Every now and then someone had sung "I am the brain of the universe"; the players had beads around their necks and brows, long hair shaking to the beat, tangling with poncho fringes. Unexpectedly one of the patients—a quiet, surly, solitary boy—had suddenly got up on the other side of the room and dived with outstretched arms toward Tamara. She had been instinctively alarmed, but rose to meet the boy on the dance floor. And without touching one another they had danced wildly, violently, unyieldingly, forgetting everything. Until they were explaining their misfortune to one another, composing their stories with their bodies; the man, to free himself from something terrible, hurls himself in his agony at the woman; she receives him with open arms but then begins to be capricious, keeps him at a distance, pretends not to notice him, flirts with strangers, turns up her nose when he approaches her; the man becomes sorrowful, tries to approach her again, is rejected and hurt, becomes gloomy and retreats within himself; then the woman in turn approaches, humoring him, and the man wants to put his arms round her, but the woman spins away, leaving him again and again, until in the end he is dancing alone, eyes closed, hands stretched above his head, face sweating from pain; then the woman suddenly returns and begins to circle with her back toward him, touching him, her hair brushing his shoulder, and finally rubbing herself against him, seeking only nearness, content with that.

It is impossible to know what the young man had experienced during the dance, but Tamara said that this was how she had felt it. In any case the boy had begun to recover after that. They had often danced together after that, but it was never the same again. They were disappointed each time. Once they even stopped in the middle of a dance, it seemed such a failure and so sad. The boy, however, had felt it his duty to ask Tamara to dance, until one evening he had caught hold of her hand and said: "We can't dance together because we're always looking for the same thing we felt then. But it won't happen again. It's too good to be copied. I won't ask you to dance again." Soon after this he'd been allowed to leave, and had waited an hour in order to say good-bye to Tamara. He was one of those who never got in touch with her afterward.

"People could dance themselves well," Tamara said. "There are lots of people who can come near others only through dancing and express themselves only by being present physically. But that's a great deal."

I asked her how, on the basis of her knowledge of people, she would classify the spruce sprig man (who incidentally was wearing something checked even then) and Tamara replied:

"He's the normal type that I don't know at all. Actually it would be interesting to get to know someone like that for a change. He's ordinary in every way. His type will soon be as rare as clean water."

She picked thoughtfully at some unevenness on her neck, then said, looking out of the window:

"It's really time I got to know some quite ordinary man. Who knows, I might like him. It's just that I've never tried. They give me the cold shivers. Ever since I was a child, as long as I can remember, I've chosen the mad, neurotic, untrustworthy and rejected the serious-minded. Those I turned my back on are now clergymen and schoolmasters, and one of them became a factory boss. But those I loved have all banged themselves against life in one way or another. I heard from my first love the other day. He's a bum in Copenhagen now, with all kinds of illnesses. Even then I chose that kind, when I was at elementary school."

"Supposing," I said, and moistened my lips to give me a little time to think (I was not quite sure of the form of my question), "supposing this is a case of consequence and not cause—how should one think of it?"

"What do you mean?" she said, her eyes narrowing. "Obviously nothing very nice."

I knew that if I made her angry she might go away and be gone for many days. But I was no longer afraid of her storms; she'd come back all right. So I continued to expound my idea. I could have said: Perhaps those you rejected found a normal woman and were thus protected. But I did not have the heart to, witty though it might have been, or for that reason. Normal is a concept which for some reason is considered absolute; it's very easy to use it to attack even those for whom it no longer exists. I decided on the contrary to flatter her a little (so poorly did I know her) and said: "Supposing you were destructive to those you have loved. You are demanding, almost to cruelty, especially to those nearest to you . . ."

I had been afraid of making her angry and to prevent it had tried to give my words a melodramatic ring. But before I had completed my sentence, she pressed her head in her hands and burst into tears. I started to get up from my chair and when at length I succeeded I started to wriggle my way across the room to console her.

She wept bitterly, her shoulders shaking, all the time it took me to cross the floor. She looked small and pitiable and I'd have liked to put my arms around her at once, to say that we are all the same, beaters-up and beaten-up, that we hurt others unknowingly, to console her with those worn words, for lack of better. But when I reached her she raised her head and said:

"I'm not well. I'm getting the curse or a cold. Maybe both. And I'm tired from being up late. The fact is staying up late doesn't agree with me. It's awful when you even have to take your sex life out of your night's sleep."

She punished me by getting up just before I reached her, went to the mirror, and looked at her tearful face.

"Funny that at my age crying so easily looks artificial. How is one going to make anybody feel sympathy?"

"Sympathy doesn't depend on that," I explained humbly from her empty chair. "It either exists or doesn't. For our species apparently it does exist. Perhaps it is through us that the bud of sympathy emerges into the universe." (This is one of my favorite ideas, I mention it whenever I get the chance, which she unsuspectingly had offered me.)

"Oh, dear," she said, patting her face, which had become blotchy. "What a universal leap. I can't keep up with you. It just struck me that life would have been different if I hadn't always been getting mixed up with visionaries. One forgets that there are positive, balanced people, even if there are

31

fewer and fewer of them. How can we mad people ever get on with each other?"

She went on patting her face irritatingly and characteristically, each pat intended to convey the message "Be thine own consoler." Then she looked at me in the mirror and said with more cruelty than for a long time:

"I'm surprised you don't praise me for saving my child from my own destructive influence. It would seem to be the logical follow-up."

Then she put on her coat and left.

I watched her walk hunched up, sniffling several times before she disappeared from sight.

I felt how her mood oppressed her. We're both unhappy after such scenes. Still we tear at each other from time to time, I don't know why. We don't need to prove anything to each other anymore. We both know well that people can always leave, abandoning each other; that's not difficult—except of course purely practically for me.

The telephone rang several times after she had gone, but I couldn't bring myself to answer it. It was Tamara they were calling, anyway.

The picture of the ordinary man, wearing a spruce sprig and something checked, thus made trouble for us right from the beginning. He was constantly in my mind like a half-finished story.

And so he was on the board of directors, was he—a bureaucrat. In addition to his ordinariness no doubt a real accumulation of social virtues.

Two days later I was gathering nettles at the back of the house when Tamara suddenly appeared at my side. She was carrying a bag from which peered a plump leek. Without speaking she took hold of my arm. We long ago gave up apologizing to one another. As far as we are concerned that's a waste of time.

"I brought you some herbal tea and some brewer's yeast, that horrible stuff," she said.

"You'll get some nettle soup soon," I said, "made from new, fresh nettles, the first this spring."

Although I knew for sure that she would come, and in just this way, directly and without evasion, her own self, I suddenly felt tremendous joy and relief. It was as if some part in the region of my heart that had shifted out of position had slipped into place again. At the same time my chest felt sore. Always when some internal stress relents the chest muscles feel tender. It is as if spirit and body are taking turns. Muscular pain always means a holiday for my spirit.

"A flycatcher and a blue tit have been fighting over that," I said, pointing to a bird house in the aspen. "The blue tit seems to have won, but all the same the flycatcher wakes me up with his song in the morning. He must be nesting somewhere near here. There seem to be more birds this spring than there have been for years. They're on the increase now that insecticides have been restricted."

"If only it would get warmer," Tamara sighed. "I've been shivering all spring. I've waited and waited, and often forgot what I was waiting for. Then I remembered that it's warmth I'm waiting for, the sun. The sun is something real. These chilly days are only temporary, to be lived through somehow—they shouldn't really be taken into account at all. Give me the shears, I'll cut some nettles by the fence."

This spring everything had grown slowly because of the cold. The aspen leaves were small and reddish, the birch buds shriveled as if they'd been fooled, deceived by a few fine days into coming out too soon. On cold nights the birds had seemed to be singing for their lives.

The weather may seem a boring topic of conversation, but one talks about it when one is in a good mood and wants to show that all is well. Discussion of the weather is typical sign language, which even people who are close to one another use at delicate moments.

We went in. I let Tamara carry the shears and the bowl full of young nettles. They go down a lot when they're cooked so that one needs plenty of them for two people. I let her help me up the steps and she seemed to appreciate this gesture. I in turn was touched by her rare helpfulness. But an atmosphere like this should not develop too far, or an unpleasant reaction may set in. It was already as if Chopin's "Funeral March" had started quietly in the background while we were climbing up the steps, slowly, bent, waves of sympathy between us; yet at the same time a secret feeling of gaiety and freedom developed its own mischievous melody.

34

The meal was quite a festive occasion. Tamara had disconnected her answering service so that we were left more or less in peace. Only some woman who remembered my number and guessed she would find Tamara here called to ask whether it was too late to write a story about spring for the ward paper. The story was already thought out, polished; it needed only to be put on paper, and every word true, from her own life.

"Yes, it's certainly worth writing," Tamara said to the telephone, "otherwise you can't get it out of your mind. Then there'll be no room for new ideas. If it's not in time for the spring number, it can go in the autumn number," she added thoughtlessly, though she is generally so careful with her words.

"But by autumn I hope I shan't be here," the woman answered, almost in tears, "and besides the subject is spring."

"Quite so," Tamara said. "I was thinking it could be published in the ward paper anyway; the writer doesn't have to be present."

"That's true in theory, but I would feel as though I'd left my soul in the clinic," the writer said.

"Write it," Tamara said. "We'll make room for it in the spring number. And do it carefully; don't forget, there must be feeling in every word. Real feeling. It will free you, that's the core of creativeness. Pain comes from stifling creativeness, not having the courage to tell. Yes, yes, you have the courage, that's exactly what you want just now. Most of what we say is telling one another about what happened to us, where we went, who we saw, what they said. That's all there is to it—don't get depressed again. I can hear it's important to you. You can pass it on to others, offer them the chance of identifying, help them. You'll be helping others, think of that."

"Your soup is getting cold," I said, greatly enjoying the combination of steaming hot broth and aesthetic discussion. Young nettles are indeed a unique experience; they should be gathered each spring at just the right moment, for a few days later the leaf stalks are tough and require long boiling, which means the aroma will suffer.

"Yes, that's right," said Tamara. "Put yourself into it. It won't touch anyone unless it touches you yourself. That's right. Keep well. Good-bye."

She was just about to put down the receiver, but the speaker had evidently not finished, because she still went on listening. Then she laughed.

"Ah, yes, always the same place," she repeated the other's words and turned to look at me, so that I knew the turn the conversation had taken. This was not the first time this had happened at the end of her conversations.

And, as always, she answered: "Not a lover, but a dear friend. The only one I have really. Yes. Well, a relation in a way, or rather a kindred spirit, a bit odd like me, only in a different way, supplementing me. Yes, we suit each other. Well, in a way. Thank you. I'll tell him."

Her soup had got quite cold, and she went and fetched more, hot from the saucepan, for herself and for me.

"She told me to be happy. And you too."

"I am. Give her my regards and wish her the same."

"She is happy and eased, though she still gets depressed sometimes. She felt for a long time that she had a hedgehog in her stomach, and now that she's got over that at last she misses it from time to time. She feels empty. It's a good subject for a spring story."

"True," I said, "true. The hedgehog is a charming creature. One would naturally become attached to it."

An unusual languor spread through my limbs. Happiness is perhaps a state of lack of tension, I thought, but immediately rejected the idea. It was too negative to hold good except in individual cases, like for example the present moment, which it did account for perfectly. But even then it required that the network of relationships surrounding it must be in balance, and that there had previously been a situation compared to which this was a change for the better. All things are conditional.

I began to explain this to Tamara, while at the same time a feeling was growing in my mind that I had not had a real erotic sensation for a long time, and that this was needed to crown my evening.

Suddenly I was in the mood to see in myself qualities I did not have. I've already stated that I detest lechery. But now I felt a desire to imagine I was a lecherous middle-aged man, fat and rich. Wealth to my mind is part of the picture of lechery; a poor man cannot be lecherous. A lecher eats and drinks a lot, and because I had just eaten well and enjoyed it very much, I could well picture how a lecher would feel after eating. We had also drunk some wine, so that side had been prepared too. Then I realized that a lecher would certainly look at the girl before him through a cloud of smoke, so I asked Tamara to bring me a cigar.

She raised her eyebrows a little at this, but fetched the cigar, and even lit it as though already part of the game.

I leaned back with the cigar between my teeth, blowing out great clouds of smoke between us. Tamara sat a little away from me, choosing a record to put on. Then she clasped her hands at the back of her neck and remained there listening, eyes half closed, one leg flung over the other. I imagined what the lecher would notice about her: the prominent knee-caps, the thighs vanishing beneath the skirt, especially their surprising and almost disproportionate thickening just where after long hesitation they finally disappeared from sight into the primal darkness. He would observe the red toenails too, where they shone so provocatively through the stockings, but he would pay little attention to the ankles and the calves, those classic parts the appreciation of which was regrettably sinking into the oblivion of history. The lecher might still be roused by a newly ironed blouse that practically cried out to

37

be rumpled; but Tamara was wearing a jersey with the top buttons carelessly left open. It was one of those garments that always look too tight and make even modest busts appear overample. It might excite the lecher's interest too. I wondered whether perhaps miserliness went along with lechery; might it be that the lecher himself would eat greedily, but would grudge his companion's every bite? Or would he offer his girl a stingy meal in some cheap joint for the sake of convention, in order to take her, afterward, to his apartment? Or would he perhaps feed her on scraps from the cupboard? Or maybe just one little glass of brandy and that from a tall-stemmed glass that might tip over at any moment? Which writer was it who wrote about a girl enraged by this very combination of miserliness and sex?—Aldous Huxley. That shows lechery does not really succeed in an atmosphere of avarice. Rather it goes with wastefulness, perhaps even generosity, and avidity, greed, perhaps overeating and noisy belching, importunity, groping.

I blew smoke into the air and felt my attempt at being a lecher vanish with it into nothing. I could not succeed in making clear to myself the core of vice—vice was an essential part of my concept of lechery—and a sad mood came over me; what should have excited seemed only wrong. I realized that emotion was a prerequisite for me and that perhaps lechery was a roundabout form of self-denial. And I remembered my divinity teacher of long ago, a minister who favored boys and openly despised girls, because he considered them stupid and frivolous. Now and then he let us ask questions about principles—he often used psychology lessons for this. "How do you free yourself from lust?" some boy always asked. And we knew what the answer would be in advance. "There are two ways," the minister would say without closing his mouth between sentences. "The first is sublimation. The second is satisfying the lust so much that it begins to disgust one."

Peace be to him in his error.

"Tamara, have you ever met a lecherous man?" I asked, getting up from my chair. I felt so weary that I wanted to throw myself on the bed and rest.

"Just a minute," she said. "I must think. Unfortunately no, at least I don't remember just now—is it a great loss?"

"I was just trying to build up for myself a picture of what lechery might be like, but I didn't manage to get very far. What do you think?"

"Well," she said, rubbing her face. "Perhaps a priest might be a lecher. Properly speaking it's a religious term. Perhaps it's a combination of religiousness and sexuality in Western culture. The name by which this exciting combination is forbidden."

"It is depravity," I said. "Women have been burned at the stake for it, women like you."

"But I'm not . . ." she began but went on: "Yes. Maybe. In a way."

She came close to me with that absent-minded look of a person trying to consider theoretically practical facts of his own existence.

But my thoughts were already elsewhere.

"Tell me what happened between you and Checks, the member of the board. What's his name by the way?"

"Mauri."

"So you met at the masquerade, eh? Did you know each other already?"

"A bit. Don't make fun of him."

So it is like that, I thought.

"So you danced with him and he danced unimaginatively, if I understand correctly, and it did not compare at all with some previous experiences, am I right?"

"It's very nice sometimes to dance just ordinarily, quietly and thoughtfully. Not always sweating like mad."

"Where had you met previously?"

"Oh, all sorts of places, here and there. But I'd never taken any notice of him, he's not the type."

"The neurotic sort?"

"No. He gives a feeling of security."

I had an irrepressible desire to whistle, a bit from the "Lambs' Polka," from the end part.

I don't know whether Tamara noticed. I remembered her own interpretation of it and felt like laughing, screaming with mirth. But I felt that for some reason she was keyed up there beside me.

"What happened between you?"

She did not answer.

I began to be so interested that my ears itched and I had to rub them thoroughly with my little fingers before I could go on.

"Did you go to his place? Or did he come to yours?"

"The answer is yes."

My God. I took the cigar from the bedside table and sucked it, but it had gone out and tasted like a cold sauna.

For a long time, for years, there had never arisen a situation when she refused to tell.

"Well, what happened?"

No answer, only her strained silence.

"Have you met him since then?"

"Yes I have, if you want to know."

"What happened between you?" I almost shouted, and to my surprise I shook her so hard by the shoulders that the bed rocked.

She looked me contentedly in the eye and said emphatically:

"Nothing."

"What?"

"Nothing."

"Nothing?"

"No."

Now I felt that I was being mocked, and this wounded me deeply. It was unfair. I am too easy a victim. But when I looked at her there was no sign of malice; she was just serious and rather strained.

"But you were together that night. You didn't come back till the morning—it was Sunday morning."

"We've been together two nights."

"But good heavens, then what have you been doing?"

"We talked."

All the next day I was confused, without being able to explain to myself what agitated me so much.

I dragged myself into the garden and tried to uproot the aspen shoots that had spread everywhere. Previously I had thought to let them grow. Actually they did not spoil the look of the fenced-in north corner, which they had taken over completely. Now I felt they should be pulled up because even old gardens in an urban area should look cared for. People might think that nobody lived in the house, that it contained only ghosts.

I did not manage to make much impression; I succeeded only in mangling a few young aspen, and their stumps by no means beautify the landscape, let alone make the garden look better. I was too restless to do even that work carefully.

I'd thought myself long immune to jealousy. Or rather jealousy was channeled in our relationship in such a way that like a flammable substance it produced warmth and light, gave birth to sensations and to nearness. Success in this matter, which people generally seem to consider impossible, had brought me to believe that sooner or later one always finds one's own path, given freedom to seek it, or is lucky as I have been. Jealousy is perhaps the wrong word entirely, so transformed is this emotion in our case. I would rather speak of reliving, identifying feelings that destroy barriers and build bridges, though negative versions of them appear in jealousy.

Of course it might be thought that I was disappointed because Tamara had not this time offered me the opportunity of reliving and identifying, which previously she had always given me, and to which over the years I had become accustomed. Undoubtedly this was one of the reasons for my agitation. In my opinion, she was acting outrageously by disappointing me. But that was not the only reason. I was troubled by a sense of danger. Everything seems to fit together too well. I don't know from what direction the blow will come and in what form. All these years I've prepared myself for the fact that one day Tamara will finally go away, that the incoherent shreds of her life will join together, and that at this stage I shall slip out of the pattern. This idea gives me no more than the familiar, solid sadness, though I know that life will then be finally over for me. It couldn't be this that I fear.

Perhaps I cannot bear to see her suffer anymore. Perhaps I'd like to see her settle down, in a thoroughly bourgeois way to our relationship, and be content with the incoherence of her life. If only I could entice her with this house and this plot of land—after all they're worth quite a lot, in a growing urban district, even if the ramshackle old house may be waiting to be condemned.

But she has said: "If I find someone someday I care for, who cares for me and who would give me security, I'll go with him, even if I have to be a runner under a sleigh."

I told her: "But I care for you and you care for me very much and I can give you security."

43

I said that in spite of everything. And she answered as I expected:

"But I don't love you. You only mean a sense of continuity to me."

She could also have said: "You're an emergency solution. Continuity for the time being. You help me to carry on."

Yet in spite of everything there is something else between us, and that indefinable something else is vital; what is missing exists in us independently of everything else, strong and without limits.

That's why we've stuck together for all these years.

A few days went past again without her coming to see me. Her telephone answering service gave me my own number when I tried to phone her. I argued, but it obstinately repeated its message, so that I finally got the impression that Tamara herself was answering.

"I can be found at the following number. . . . I can be found at the following number. . . ." rang in my mind for days, until even that seemed satisfying, as if she had assured me that she was constantly with me in spirit; her body in London, her heart in Greece, like Byron.

I tried to concentrate on my work and, surprisingly enough, succeeded in doing so. I had been annoyed by an article in the *Literary Review* which, to my mind, wrongly emphasized the share of imagination in the creation of fiction, and I determined to reply. To my way of thinking a writer never builds from nothing, he builds from material most significant to him at the moment. If he does not, his work is of no consequence to himself or to others. True, there are very skillful bluffers, and if the result is good, nobody can criticize it. They are beyond criticism, as all truly significant works are. Their title pages should carry the words "Not for Critics."

I slipped into my article in toto the words Tamara had rattled off on the telephone while her nettle soup was getting cold, and this warmed me. It was unlikely that she even remembered what she had said; intuition goes straight to the heart of the problem while intellect stumbles up the staircase of knowledge.

I concluded that Tamara's philological studies had not been wasted, although she had not continued in the field. In her present work she needs all kinds of knowledge. It would not have been a bad thing if at some stage she had studied law, as her father had apparently desired, or theology, her mother's dream, and worked for some years as a missionary—which she as a schoolgirl had considered the noblest vocation. (This is incidentally almost all I know about her background, except for general historical events, such as the war, and personal states of mind connected with it. We tend to ignore these nowadays even though the generation growing now is the first I hope to have the right to omit this chapter from their life stories.)

I pictured Tamara in a white dress, her hair drawn back tightly, her nervous unpainted lips chapped (as they always get chapped when unpainted), the lines on her forehead clearly visible, shouldering the cross that would lead her through this vale of sorrow. She would speak of sin, of self-denial, the stifling of the lusts of the flesh, and would undoubtedly do so with great abandonment and sincerity. She would be in an excellent position to imagine all the temptations that man is faced with. How enviable the world of the believer, she once said, seeing lust and temptations on all sides; certainly one wouldn't have time to get bored. They must be true adventurers, all of them.

And I imagined how she would try to mortify the flesh:

she would lie with her husband only twice a week, after Luther's example, she would use cold towels, remember the Finnish winter and icy swims, write long letters to her homeland, begin to practice yoga and vegetarianism; or if she was not married, if they all had wives with them—Tamara doesn't sleep with men whose wives she knows: "even my immorality has some limits"—she would continually pray: O Lord, deliver me from these fantasies, test me not further, what is Thy purpose, O Lord? She would be in agony, would swim amid crocodiles, lust after snakes, repent, start to look transparent, grow black tulips. She would find me outside the village, my legs shattered by an American jeep, but the rest of my body uninjured. . . . And in time we would realize that we had the same kind of imagination, and that it was quite natural for her to do what I imagined; and she would climb on top of me, sit on my thighs and put me into herself, thinking of the words in the Bible: And God created them man and woman.

Tamara came in at four o'clock in the morning. I thought at first I'd been awakened by the blackbird's song. Then I realized she was beside me. I had waited up for her quite late, and even in bed had stayed awake thinking of all kinds of things, so that when she did come I had been sleeping heavily like the neglected foolish virgins tired out from intensive waiting for the bridegroom. She had her own key, so that she could come at any time of the day or night. It was good to feel that she was there, and the thought of reproaching her did not cross my mind; time is too short for that. Though sometimes I should have. Few things are more agonizing than waiting. Tamara herself can't bear waiting. I suffer from it only occasionally in an acute form, when I am filled with uncertainty.

When she came like this at night she usually started to tell me everything on her own initiative. She'd be full of her fresh experience, carrying it naked, hardly realizing that she was clothing it with words and voice. She'd seem to open herself, allowing me to share her sensation, and then I always felt that I was a part of her, a part of her brain, her body, and her sex, object and actor; that she held out her experience like a fruit and let me eat of it, just like man's first sexual illumination in the Bible. (I don't know why the Bible haunts my mind in this way.) And we'd both grow moist in its juice.

That's how she avoids the pain and loneliness that is always connected with parting; she told me this years ago.

"How are you?" she said, her lips against my neck.

"Fine. Now. And you?"

"Fine. Really fine."

She ran her hand down my stomach, feeling between my legs as if confirming that the same familiar insignificant undergrowth was still there, admitting its emotional value. I remembered again how she had once massaged my thighs evening after evening, while we both hoped for a miracle. She had been on her knees between my legs, rubbing her face against me, her hair spreading over my stomach, getting entangled in everything she did. She had read oriental text-books and studied the peculiar nuances of *auparistaka* and fellatio, discovered how geishas rouse jaded men and where the nerves run on either side of the stomach. I believe she became very skillful, in spite of her striking lack of result with me. I tried to thank her in many ways. But I had hardly touched her before she said: "Stop that fingering around, I don't need a man for that. It's no use serving me bones, I need meat there." And when I tried to kiss and lick her with my tongue, she soon moved away, saying: "Okay, okay. It feels nice all right, but it's only the preliminaries. I want the man inside me quick, and for a long time."

No other part of me would do for her except the one that was not available.

Until we were driven to this: that she came to me after she was satisfied.

No, "driven to" is the wrong expression. We sought a way

that would suit us and in the end we found it; our frank search was rewarded; we invented this unique pleasure.

"Why didn't you stay till morning?" I asked—time always interests me.

"He had to go."

I felt her with my finger. She was like a glue bottle, dried up on the surface, slippery within.

"So you didn't just talk this time."

Evidently she did not follow my logic at all, since she said with surprise:

"No, we didn't talk. Who said we did?"

I was taken aback for a moment, and, cautiously, I decided to approach the subject from another angle.

"Well, what was he wearing this time?"

"Just a minute," she said, yawning against my chest. "Dark gray suit with faint stripe, pale yellow shirt and tie with quiet yellow dots, no undervest—men have stopped wearing them, thank goodness, a sure sign the Finnish summer has started— dark blue shorts and black socks. Nothing to object to."

"So no checks this time?"

Tamara laughed.

"No, you're quite impossible, you really have become absent-minded. You're mixing up two different people again. I haven't been with *him* now."

I realized that *he* had so filled my thoughts that I hadn't been able to imagine Tamara with anyone else lately. I felt relieved and mortified at the same time. Even annoyed, so much so that reliving her experience seemed far beyond achievement.

Father Andres was in Copenhagen, I thought. Then there were the crazy intellectuals, the whole flock of neurotics, the real rulers of her heart—it might be any one of them.

"It was the long, half-hard one," Tamara said, as if sensing the hopeless straying of my thoughts.

"You mean the Capitalist!"

49

How could I have left him out of my calculations? Tamara met him every now and again when the opportunity occurred. Imagine, she told me, a surprisingly unprejudiced, substantial businessman, rich and progressive, the peak of my career.

And I tried to imagine, but somehow the situation did not please me at all. I couldn't even take pleasure in the fact that I had guessed right, which usually gives me a special delight. In the first place I was not prepared tonight to identify with the Capitalist. Secondly I noticed suddenly that I was jealous on behalf of the object of my jealousy.

And I said: "How can you in this day and age bring yourself to go to bed with a capitalist? Don't you feel ashamed?"

I sensed that Tamara's eyes widened in the darkness as she shifted away from me.

"But they're just the ones that are in the worst position in the modern world. Nobody's sorry for them. The bottom of their world's fallen out, they've lost their sense of purpose. The bells have already tolled for them. But how can they help the fact that they're born into that position in society? They need all possible sympathy."

I could imagine how her eyes sparked there on the other side of the bed.

After a little while I put out my hand humbly and drew her back beside me. I didn't even know whether her front or her back was toward me; she was just the soft warm bundle that for some incomprehensible reason I wanted to possess.

"I'm very happy that he found rest with me, even for a moment," Tamara murmured between my kisses.

*L*ater I was proud that I had recognized the Capitalist at once by the distinguishing features mentioned. With him, stiffening does not occur throughout the whole length; the extremity remains soft. This, however, is in no way a handicap, it only gives its own peculiar effect to the business. Father Andres's is flat-topped and angular like a chisel. With some men the extremity is arrow-shaped, with indentations on either side that are as hard as the gills of a fish. "But what I don't understand is why in some cases it's curled up," complains Tamara. "It seems very poorly made, as if in some spots there were only string instead of a rubber band. Not that it makes any difference in practice. I've seen some that knock on the stomach, others that point straight out like a steelyard, and some can swing it around forty-five degrees. But it's always beautiful and interesting, even when it's small and limp like that of Michelangelo's dying warriors, she said, thus magnanimously bringing even me into the picture.

51

I listened to this as to *The Thousand and One Nights*, regretting that in the days when all this was concretely within my scope I had not observed more, studied the matter more carefully, given more attention to it. I'd often been unforgivably hasty, had imagined for instance that vehemence was a sign of passion, and that therefore men should always be vehement. This is not to say that the ultimate exertion does not have its own relish, and in these times a great deal of merit as exercise. I anticipate the day when gymnasia are established where this kind of exercise is offered, either by means of impersonal apparatus, or more personality along with tea and sympathy. When my celibacy had lasted a while I missed not only the satisfaction but also the holds, positions, movements, wrestling, the sensation of the blood circulating, the sweating, even the creaking and shaking of the bed, that reeling as if one were clearing the crossbar, or lifting four hundred pounds above the chest and holding it, feet close together, above the head for a moment; and besides all this I missed the complete exhaustion. Only those who are denied it know its value. On the whole I've despised athletic performances, but from this point of view I understand them. How I would have skied if only my legs had been at my disposal, and what a fervent jogger the local landscape lost in me. It may be that if there had been no Tamara these streets would have seen of an evening a sprightly, track-suited walker on his hands.

"And what about Checks—what was his name again?"

"Mauri."

"Well, what's happened to him lately?"

"He's skiing."

"Skiing? At this time of year? In the North or in the South?" (Once again our thoughts had been running along the same track.)

"I don't know. He never tells me where he's going. Maybe in the North. He said this was the last chance to ski."

"And you went straight off to the Capitalist?"

"What else can I do when I'm waiting?"

Then I thought it was a suitable moment to take the bull by the horns again.

"You haven't told me even once what it's like with Mauri."

"And I won't. Not at the moment anyway. Maybe never."

"That's not fair. I'm jealous."

And it was true: after feeling jealous for Mauri a while ago because of the Capitalist, I suddenly found myself accepting the Capitalist and considering him quite harmless, even uninteresting, whereas thinking of Mauri filled me with new, fresh jealousy, exciting and unbearable. It was years since Tamara had refused to talk.

"What's he like? Long? Serpentine? Knobby? Serrated? Hidden like a dog's or a shy German officer's?"

"Now you're being disgusting," Tamara said. "If you're going to descend to that level I'll never tell you anything anymore."

And in the early morning light I saw how she pinched her mouth shut in a way that no magic sesame would open.

"I am sorry," I said. "I didn't mean to hurt you."

"That's just what you did mean—to hurt and be crude. But I won't stand it. And I particularly can't stand this casual and unconscious hurting. You must hurt deliberately and knowingly. Then there's some good in it both for yourself and for the other. The other person learns his limits and I inform him of my own. That's fair. But you strike out blindly, not knowing what you're after, and use expressions you yourself don't approve of."

"You're right. But don't you understand that it pains me when you suddenly refuse to speak, after all these years."

That remark about the years was unfair again and melodramatic, but she seemed to accept it.

"Don't you understand that sometimes one wants to keep a thing to oneself? There are times when one wants to push something into the farthest corner of one's soul and let it mature there before one even begins to think. And besides,

I haven't anything to tell that would interest you. We've met, but only to talk. It's hard to repeat talk. And it wouldn't interest you. He's a very matter-of-fact and dull sort of man."

Good God, I thought, shutting my eyes, good God. If only she knew how each word made me suffer. Was it really so serious, really so serious. . . ? In imagination I got out of bed, put my bare feet on the floor, walked to the window, opened it, and breathed in deeply.

"It's suffocating here," Tamara said. "Do you mind if I open the window?"

"No," I said, "I feel the same way."

I watched as she walked, a white figure, across the room, opened the window, and remained there breathing in the fresh air. Bird song flooded into the room as if it were inseparable from the fresh air.

"There *are* more birds this summer, I've noticed it too," Tamara said. "Have you thought about where we should spend the summer? Should we try and find a deserted farmhouse that still feels lived in? Somewhere in the North or wherever you like. Funny, we completely forgot to think about it this spring."

"Maybe you don't want to go anywhere this summer," I replied, prepared for any kind of disappointment.

"Perhaps. Or—yes, I want to really, but without romanticizing it this time as I have before. I don't really know why. Maybe it's because I don't feel as alienated as before. Alienated people romanticize everything and imagine they've discovered everything themselves and for the first time. And for them that could be so. That's the way all kinds of new trends get started—neoemotionalism, neoprimitivism—and that's all right, no harm in names if they give us the courage to be more varied. I've been thinking that with things developing so quickly nowadays people have to go through more stages than they used to. In a way it's like living longer. I'm sure if people knew they were going to live for three hundred years they'd look at things differently. They'd take better care of nature. This generation that still has its roots in the countryside ought to live for three hundred years. Children that are used to streets and asphalt yards don't think it's important to save swamps and forests. They don't even know there are such things. One of the girls in our ward gets hysterical whenever she's on a path. But she feels safe on a street."

While she was talking I thought about the way in which windows affect people's mental activity. People must certainly think most of their thoughts while they are looking out of a window. Or in bed.

"You'll get cold there by the window," I said, my throat dry but my mind for some reason moved and grateful, though I couldn't express this. "The spring air is treacherous."

"Shall I leave the window open a bit?"

"Yes, do."

She turned to come back to me; she was shivery, her skin all goose flesh, the hairs standing like down on her arms, nipples puckered with cold, her toes frozen.

I would have liked to tell her that I was interested in their conversations too, and I was sure she could repeat them very well. But I didn't dare. She curled up against me, her ice-cold feet on my stomach just in the place where there was still some feeling. And I warmed her. And we slept.

In spite of the pleasure that her mere nearness brought me, I couldn't help feeling afterward that she had rejected me; it was cruel to deny me the sensation I craved. The meeting with the Capitalist seemed altogether too casual to satisfy me. I wanted to identify with the person who most occupied her mind. I did find out that he had come back from his skiing holiday.

"What's his surname?"

"I won't tell you."

"In that case I shall start calling him Kustaa Mauri Armfelt, after the famous philanderer and diplomat, the Alcibiades of the North."

And I kept my word, mean as it may seem.

Tamara was fretful, as always before her period, and wandered around with her papers from place to place. She was supposed to start off a discussion on the subject of our basic needs of expression and the mechanisms that stifle them. There was not much time for preparation, and none for deliberation, as usual.

"I've thought about these things over and over, and talked about them a million times, but now everything seems to disintegrate in my mind. My brain's stopped completely. I can't even distinguish colors, I only *know* that's green." She pointed at my ancient faded tea cozy. "Men don't know anything about this rhythm."

"Is it such a great loss?" I said, risking her displeasure, for I was interested in the matter.

She sighed and rubbed her face with both hands. I guessed that I was to her at that moment some lower creature that had no chance at all of understanding the ranges of a vastly superior and more complex being, even if it should stoop so far as to reveal them.

"Don't you realize it's a part of creativity? Woman is biologically so creative that she never needs to prove it. She may feel some primitive frustration at having to be emptied once a month, but the sight of her own blood is a relief for a woman nowadays. I always feel well then and wild, but that may be a recent layer in me, a result of the traumas of watching the calendar in my girlhood. I'm quite sure this cycle is connected with some larger natural system, just as the atom is the solar system in microcosm."

"But in that case it should happen to all women at the same time."

"Not at all. That just shows you don't understand anything. Each one of us is of course at a different point in the spiral of life."

There was no argument to raise against this, so I took the cozy from the tea pot and poured myself a cup of steaming, perfectly brewed herbal tea. It was fresh, just arrived from Germany, ordered for me by the health-food store and quite different from the dry old stuff they keep on the shelves, smelling of mouse piss.

"Would you like some?"

"No, thanks. Don't you remember that when I'm in this state I can't stand the smell?"

She changed her position on the sofa, where she had established herself to prepare her lecture; some of her papers were spread over the floor around her. She looked very beautiful lying on her back, papers and pen in her right hand, dictionary and English periodical on her midriff, a big pile of books on the floor near her head, and typewritten sheets around her on the cushions and the floor. I could not help suddenly thinking what a dangerous combination brains and femininity were, more dangerous than anyone dared imagine or admit, and how much depended on the direction of the energy concealed in this combination.

"I feel terrible," she complained. "My whole circulation is concentrated in my pelvis. I can't think. Just look—my stomach's like an inflated bladder. And it's particularly difficult when there's a full moon and a wind, like now."

I looked at her stomach arching against her close-fitting dress, and it was true that it did stand out clearly, especially since she held it on either side with her hands like half a melon. And I could not help wondering what it would be like if there were a child there, my child, whose growth inside her she would observe and describe from day to day. And I would follow the swelling of her stomach, and nobody would notice it at first except me. Then it would begin to protrude a little through her clothes, and her way of walking would gradually change as her center of gravity shifted. Finally it would be really enormous so that everyone would instinctively leap aside and I would walk before her waving an imaginary flag and shouting "Make way, here comes the woman who bears my child." And she would advance like the world's first automobile, stomach in front, leaning back, head up, in her eyes an omnipotent, omniscient, drowsy look that nothing could disturb. And I, who could experience this immensity only through imagination, would breathe humbly and quietly, so quietly that there was no possible chance of her hearing: Do not take this experience away from us, O Mistresses, you cruel and merciless rulers of life, you who seek from us security and permanence. Who will guarantee our permanence, protect for us our right to new lives, permit us to follow their development if only from the sidelines, who if not you, O Goddesses?

Maybe herbal tea makes me a little dramatic. I remember praying, speaking with spirits, chatting with gods while drinking it, just as Tamara claims she always starts singing after one bottle of beer. But I am used to allowing myself freedom in the realm of imagination. I don't even disclose my most secret thoughts to Tamara, because I know she would laugh at them. My most secret thoughts are always deadly serious, grave and earnest, messengers from the far-off land where tragedy and comedy couple in deepest silence. That is why one of them, dragged into daylight alone, often seems an orphan—is refractory, stumbles and blushes—until the other comes to the rescue.

My mind returned to the real subject. "Isn't all that exhausting psychophysical process rather a drawback to creativity? The brain stops working, the body swells up, the emotional life is thrown off balance. I don't really understand what the advantages are."

Tamara raised herself on her right elbow and looked at me as if I were a polyp.

"Being emptied is a condition of creativity. In woman this occurs through the opening of the ducts. Once a month she bleeds, once a month the ovum leaves her, milk comes from her breasts, in birth she is torn completely, she weeps more frequently than a man, her tear ducts are in more constant use, and in addition she sweats and evacuates."

"But a man does that too—any man," I said bravely, aware that even that was not simple in my case. "Besides, men vomit quite often. And once when I was a child my ear discharged. Many men have a chronic cold."

"Surely you must understand what I mean. A woman keeps open, she's always beginning again from the beginning, renewed. I know that after this I'll be in great form again. Everything will seem new and interesting. Men just clog up. Of course they have their lovely sperm—I'll certainly not say anything bad about that; it should be sold in jars and mixed in face creams, there's nothing better for the skin."

"Surely not externally . . ."

"It might be good externally too—not everyone has the chance to use it internally. And think what it does in a woman's body—it roams around in her. In twelve hours it passes through her whole body and is expelled in her breathing."

I did not argue with this. I often smelled the odor of sperm on her breath long before twelve hours had passed. "A woman is like earth," I had said then, "she either bears fruit or decomposes everything." And she had answered: "Generations are rotting in me before they are born. When I die I'll be united with them, my children."

And I had felt an inconsolable sense of being outside, had caught hold of her and asked: "But where is my place in this cycle? Even I am not completely a bystander; surely I have some task?" And she had replied: "You are my child. Always and eternally you men are our children. We give birth to you ourselves and take turns in rocking you to sleep. Everything else is wrong. You look for a mother in us. Or perhaps not a mother. What you're looking for is just once to break this cycle, this curse of being born of woman, which you never recover from—that's what you look for in a woman. For a man, every woman is a mother, and with every woman he dreams of breaking this eternal cycle for a moment. But he never succeeds. That's his cross."

"What is a woman's cross?" I said aloud, returning to the old question.

As if she had followed my train of thought, Tamara answered:

"A woman's cross is the burden of two kinds of creativity. And she can never escape it either."

"Except if people are bred someday in test tubes and incubators."

"Except then."

She turned on her stomach and both the dictionary and *Adult Education* slipped to the floor.

"It would be interesting to see whether women will give up this role," she said. "There may come a time when they'll fight tooth and nail for the right to breed their children themselves."

Her words astonished me, and I would have liked to make some remark about her own attitude toward motherhood. But I kept my mouth shut. We had a mutual agreement, long ago put into words, now unspoken, that we would leave each other's past alone and speak only of the area that was common to both of us. At our age, people already have all kinds of entanglements which no amount of words will change. If there was one thing we were totally agreed upon, it was to draw a line at our pasts.

"Poor men," I sighed involuntarily, and thought that this universal, ever-true formula would suitably close the conversation. But Tamara was all wound up and continued.

"Whatever town I go to, my heart is always wrenched at the sight of the half-drunk men lounging on the benches under the birch trees, and the lonely fellows staggering along the emptying streets at the weekend—fellows with no home to welcome them. It's home they are longing for. Perhaps they've always been sent out, ever since they were boys and the house was being cleaned. They've never had the chance to be masters at home except when they were furious, drunk— then they had the nerve. And then they throw everyone else out. I've spoken to them—do you think I don't know what I'm talking about? Keeping them as out-patients doesn't help if they don't have a home to go to. That's how much progress we've made. I've often thought of sending one of them here—

61

you have plenty of rooms, though rooms don't make a home."

"The man with no hands does come here to rake. And then there is the regular knife grinder who comes around. And when that woman whose boy didn't want to go to school lived here for two weeks, I couldn't get a thing done. I need to be alone. I have my modest demands too."

"I know," Tamara said, "but when one is worried one thinks of all kinds of things. In my mind I've founded innumerable communes here. You don't know what interesting people you could live with."

"I believe you, I believe you. Thank you all the same, but I don't need people, not at all. It's quite enough for me to hear about them from you."

"If women only knew how weak men are, how sensitive . . ."

"Yes," I said, and felt as if my paralyzed legs had shivered with emotion; every now and then they undergo a sensation of this kind. (I often have dreams in which I walk and run, or fall on my feet after hanging for a long time. And I quite often dream that I expose myself to an admiring crowd. Contrary to what one would think, I am generally in a good and balanced mood when I wake from such dreams. What an exhibitionist the world is losing in me!)

Tamara sat up, twisted her long hair into a knot by winding it around the fingers of one hand, searched for long hairpins in her bag, gathered them in her lap, and started to fix her hair, running her hands over her bowed head to check what she had accomplished. Her movements and attitude reminded me of my grandmother, a tough little woman who lived to be ninety, bringing up seven children and burying three. In other circumstances Tamara could have been the mother of a large family, one child at her breast, another in the cradle, a third hanging on to her skirt. She would have been one of those who are spared childbed fever and avoid inflammation of the breasts, who give birth while digging up potatoes and breast-feed during meals, whose absence is a cloud and for whose return even the path home cries.

I don't know whether men or creatures like myself have cycles, but whenever Tamara is in this mood, claiming the laws of the universe for herself, I am overwhelmed by a helpless pathos, a combination of pomposity and remoteness, as if a blend of drinks that do not mix had gone to my head. In other circumstances I too might have kept away from people on a day like this, or got really drunk, stuck a knife into the table up to the hilt and commanded the old woman and the kids to shut up, fingering the sticks of dynamite in my trouser pocket.

She pattered barefoot across the floor from place to place, quite unnecessarily to my mind, and her bottom quivered under her limp dress just as in my childhood the uncorseted hams of country women had wobbled under their summer frocks when they came to the village. These recollections made me feel a little better, and to cheer myself up further I reminded myself of the big boys' stories about plump servant girls when they met in the evening to go on a spree with a bottle of pop and a dozen glasses.

To my surprise Tamara was not going out. It transpired that she had come to spend her bad day with me. Besides, it was Saturday evening, so there was really nothing else to do anyway, and she never went out just for the sake of going out. It was real family weather too: dry, cloudy but fine.

"You really ought to be out of doors more," she said in a bustling tone that boded no good.

"I've already been out today," I lied. "And on top of that I walked around the house three times on my hands."

She looked at me and scratched her nose, and I prayed silently that she would not decide to start dragging me around the streets. Once or twice a year she had a fit of doing that, and I had noticed that it happened when she was at this particular stage of her universal system. Or she got a sudden desire to clean out the place for me, and dragged everything out of drawers and off shelves, tore up clothes of mine still in good condition for rags, so that I could have wept if I had dared, as she destroyed the few bits of clothing I really felt at home in. For instance, my old dark brown velvet jacket was the only one in which I could write. She claimed that it stunk and burned it before my eyes. For me its smell excited the imagination, and it was a long time before I got used to writing in any other jacket. Nowadays I don't let her see the clothes in which I actually work. They have all become adapted to my nature, they are well-worn friends and smell familiar. In a locked drawer of my desk I keep an old fur hat which I wear on damp spring and autumn evenings to keep my head warm. Sometimes it seems as if the chill in my legs steals slyly upward and gets into my brain. I often get cold sitting at my typewriter. While I am working I wear red-, black-, and yellow-striped felt boots—but these I don't need to hide, because Tamara herself bought them for me in some shop specializing in neo-folk stuff. I don't think they make me look beautiful either, but at least she accepts them.

So you see we do have slight differences of opinion in our relationship. If we didn't, I would feel that we were abnormal, deviates, people whom others would have the right to wonder at and fail to understand.

Once on a day like this some years ago, Tamara decided to start putting the garden in order, and with a hoe chopped out preliminary plans all over the yard. From the gate to the steps there was to be a graveled path edged with rich borders of stock and cosmos. On the lawn there were also to be circles here and there from which flowers would burst as if thrown up by the earth; mignonettes and arabis would reward every stray footfall. The bumps she managed to make can still be discerned under the sorrel and the fine tufted blades of purple rushes; the dry, sandy soil will long remember its dream. But every spring there is the consolation of the bulbs: the humility of the scillas, the stubborn delicacy of the pusch-kinias, the erect, candid grace of the crocuses. Faithful as a bulb, I used to think when I looked at them. Then there came a year when the moles multiplied and rampaged, and in one winter they ate the whole slope clean as a whistle. Only a few bent, unsymmetrical tulip leaves came through, but no flowers. It seemed to me spring did not come at all that year. We managed somehow or other to get to summer, and I lived through that only so I could put in new bulbs in the autumn. I spent a whole week crawling about on the ground. I planted hundreds of bulbs. I stuck a rattle in the earth. I noticed that neighbors were using exhaust gas. I thought of using it too, but then I dreamed that I was treading on moles, stunned and fleeing in all directions, their insides bursting out colorfully from their bodies, and after that I could not continue my measures against them. Instead, I called on magic spells and Greek mythology; "Persephone, return. . . ." And spring rewarded me. The house appeared to be floating on flowers. It seems to me that in those weeks we only sighed, unaccustomed to the rare experience of superabundant beauty. For some reason I do not long for flowers in the middle of the summer; the sovereign greenness is enough for me. Only the old peonies in their corner feel it their duty to blossom more abundantly from summer to summer.

Tamara sat at the typewriter with closed eyes, rubbing her temples. After a while she began to write, and it seemed that at last she had really got started. I determined to keep silent until she spoke. She said she could write best when I was present without reminding her of my existence. She has sometimes philosophized about this. "Nearness is not always talking—in fact it's very rarely that. Nearness is a message from one skin to another; just by being in the same room, the same house, our bodies exchange particles. You know that feeling of a place that is not lived in. It's a concrete thing. That's how a baby senses aloneness or nearness. It doesn't even know what's in question, but if its body doesn't receive messages of human presence it begins to cry. For this reason physical presence is important, and how long it lasts. When one loves, one wants to be together a lot. It's as simple as that. My life is full of people who've been rejected when they were small. Human life is a matter of love relationships right from the start. If you're near while I'm working, my body realizes your nearness and is at ease, untroubled, and I can use all my energy for thinking."

I knew very well that this was not always so. Often she was not able to concentrate and accused me of bothering her. She went away impatiently and hurriedly, as if she couldn't bear a moment longer to be near me. Perhaps the particles of our bodies bombarded each other at such times, eagerly engaged in a snowball fight. This time, however, it seemed that I was needed, and I tried to make my nearness radiate nonexistence as much as possible. I selected something quiet to read, something that would not tempt me to speak. We were never able both to work at the same time. For some reason I again chose Greek mythology, but this time for safety's sake about lesser gods, the forgotten little Graces.

I had evidently fallen asleep in my chair and had a dream that it was raining; after the dry, chilly spring a soft rain had come at last, dropping sleepily on the roof, swelling the buds in a moment, opening the still-folded leaves, spreading those that had already opened, and wonderfully relieving the mind of man as if it too had only been waiting for the holy water of spring to dare open, begin new growth. Finally I went out in the rain to swim, wading up to my knees in the water while the rain tinkled around me on its surface; as always when observed from close up, the drops seemed to bounce upward, dancing for a moment in the air in time to their own music. The shore was muddy and I sank in at first, but then I felt under my feet a hard sandy bottom, and I waded along it, filled with great joy. The lake opened out, the reeds ended, and in the distance I saw some cows that had waded into the water up to their bellies; I threw myself in and swam in the rain, with someone—perhaps Tamara—swimming near me, pushing little waves against me. Suddenly, in the dream, I was sure that I had seen this place somewhere, experienced it, and I was just about to remember where when I awoke.

66

Tamara had finished writing and came toward me, reaching out to me with her arms and her body. I felt for a moment quite distinctly how the levels of sleep and waking slowly changed places in my consciousness, neither vanishing nor replacing the other completely.

"I had a good dream," I said, and put my arm around her. "I was just about to find out whether you were in it or not. Thank goodness the dream didn't take you away with it, as it took the lake and my ability to swim," I said, burying my face against her thigh, tickling her with my nose. "And I dreamed it was raining, and that too seemed good; the whole dream was full of feelings, it was altogether an erotic landscape—a shame to leave it. But I always choose the place where you are."

"But you did get your rain," Tamara said. "It's raining now."

Her voice was soft and relaxed. She sat down on the floor by my chair and put her head in my lap. Then she took the hairpins out and shook her hair. It fell over my knees.

"I feel better now. I feel better in every way. I wrote ten pages. It's done now. My whole body feels as if it's been whipped. I always work with my whole body. My shoulders feel quite tender."

"If only I could lift you in my arms and carry you to bed. I'm always dreaming of doing that," I found myself saying, still half in my dream.

"I'll carry you," Tamara said. "Let him carry who is strong enough. I'm strong enough for anything now."

And before I had time to answer, she had picked me up and carried me to bed. She managed very well, though she was only just strong enough; this was not the first time, but it was unusual.

She seemed excited by her achievement, and began to play with me as if I were some rare quarry which, after long waiting in ambush, she had finally managed to catch. I knew that I was not the only cause for this, nor even the heroic feat of carrying me, but the joy and relief that she felt at completing her work. Perhaps her hormone function also changed at that moment—who can say for certain. She unraveled me like a cat does a ball of wool. She opened my belt and pushed her hand under my clothes. Her fingers were cold from typing, and she warmed them against my skin, waking me, rubbed her face against me as was her habit, fussed and romped, and my body listened to all this as if still in a dream, unwilling to wake completely for fear that she might vanish with the dream. I felt as if a little child or some animal were playing on me, twisting and nibbling and finally stretching itself to rest on my stomach, having decided to sleep there; she knows that I like the sensation of weight, it relaxes me. She had warmed up and was panting with exhaustion. Encouraged by her high spirits, I pushed my fingers into her, then looked at them. They were red. I turned her on her back and pulled myself to my knees between her legs. It took time, but she waited patiently and finally I succeeded. I kissed her stomach and many other spots which to my mind do not have sufficiently beautiful names. I caressed her in the modest ways that I knew and some new ones that to my surprise I invented on the spur of the moment. I looked at the slow stain on the sheet beneath her. I remembered that she too is a bed-clothes fetishist, and loves expressive sheets. She has often threatened to enter her compositions in the spring exhibition for amateurs arranged by the art club of the high school patrons' association. I dipped my finger in her as in an inkwell, and wrote on the sheet in big red letters: TAMARA. Above it spread her own mark like a chopped-up heart turned upside down, like a ragged cloud.

"How is Kustaa Mauri Armfelt these days?"

"He's at a dog show."

I was interested at once.

"Yes, of course, he likes dogs. What kind . . . ?"

"He doesn't like dogs, he likes Doberman pinschers. Anyone who has ever had anything to do with them will never be satisfied with any other breed. They never become really tame, they obey just for form's sake, to show their contempt for people. It seems they especially despise women because now and then they reveal to women their need for tenderness. They obey their master blindly."

"They must be very like their master. Does he have more than one?"

"Two. They're pedigreed dogs. He soon won't know what to do with all the prizes they win."

"And they approve of you?"

"No, they don't. They scowl at me whenever he's not looking. And I scowl back. He says I annoy them, that they're

69

not used to behavior like that. But sometimes he tells them to be quiet and makes me stroke them."

"And how do they react to that?"

"They're quiet, but they look at me out of the corner of their eyes. I'm sure they'd tear me to shreds in a couple of minutes if they dared and had the chance."

"Where do you meet them?"

"When he takes them for a walk. Sometimes he brings them to my place, sometimes we go for a walk together. And a few times I've helped when he's training them. But that doesn't really work. He says they hate me instinctively, that they're jealous."

"Why aren't you going to the show?" I said. (You see how anxious I was to bring them together again, to arrange a situation in my mind. A dog show would have been a suitably exotic milieu: racial purity, champions, barking, growling of the males, some silly bitch in heat spoiling everything, quiet and deliberate words of command, enthusiastic civilized people, breeding films in the evening, the game of victory and loss, an air of excitement and festivity.)

"It wouldn't do. People go there with their families, it's a family affair. Besides, he always keeps the dogs away from me before a show nowadays; he says I have a disturbing effect on their emotional lives."

"What is his wife like?"

"I don't know and I wouldn't want to. I protect myself from that kind of information. I do know she's on the board of the Women's Committee of the Doberman Pinscher Association. And that the dogs apparently love her—they lick her and nibble the tips of her ears."

"Does he do that too?"

"I don't want to know, I don't want to know anything about their relationship," Tamara said vehemently. And it seemed to me that the downy hairs that every now and then appeared on her upper lip bristled slightly. "I've got some morals after all."

"What do you mean by morals?"

"I don't go with men whose wives I know."

I would have liked to answer with a joke or to whistle a bit of the "Lambs' Polka," as its rhythm would have suited our conversation, but I didn't have the heart. I thought of how Tamara's attitude had changed over the years I had known her, how it had started out from great, uncompromising isolation and ended up in a maze of small conditions. How she had had to adapt and recognize herself, amazed that she was still a human being; how she had finally admitted unpredictability, confessed it humbly. And how I loved her for it.

"Are they hard to find?" I said clumsily. "I mean men like that."

"Not really. Every now and then you run into one. But often they eventually want to bring their wives into the picture. And it's funny," she continued with sudden interest, "that it often happens at a point when you'd least expect it. It seems as if they suddenly want to throw their whole brood in my lap—this is my family, love them too. As you know, Father Andres has some sort of wife and two children in Denmark. They live together with several other young families in some kind of community, as they call it. And all the time he's talked about wanting to come to Finland with his family, to show them all to me, the whole caboodle—he's sure I'd like his wife. I don't doubt it. I told him the whole gang is welcome, and at the same time said a silent farewell to Father Andres, a bit sadly I don't deny. You remember what he was like, young, crazy, and excited by the sense of sin as only a Catholic can be. It took me a long time before I realized he felt guilty toward his wife; I forget they always do, that's the dark side of marriages for love. Perhaps coming to Finland would have been some sort of sacrificial offering or symbolic confession. But it fell through, and just as well."

"Surely you don't need to hate those wives so much," I said, as tempting dramas began to unfold before my mind's eye.

71

"But I don't hate them—on the contrary, I respect them, now and then," Tamara answered, shifting the hot-water bottle from her left cheek to her right; she always had sinus trouble in the spring, although her sinuses were so clean that there was nothing the doctors could do but admire the X rays in the light of the spring sun. "But talking of wives, I always feel somehow outlawed, almost indecent, in spite of the fact that I've given a lot of pleasure to many depressed men and sent them home in a good mood. Nowadays the single woman doesn't even have the rights or status of a courtesan; they were cultured, respected women in their time, better educated than wives. When I'm with men I feel equal."

"So Father Andres was coming here with his family, was he?" I asked, for my thoughts were still spinning around this subject.

"Yes, he was, but he isn't anymore. Don't you worry about that. Though it would have been interesting for you to meet him."

"No thank you," I said. "I'm not interested in meeting your men. I have my own morality and my own limitations. I enjoy hearing your descriptions of them—I would even say they are vital for me—but I don't want to meet them."

"There you are. There it is. All right, don't try and understand me."

"But I do understand you, I understood all the time, right from the beginning."

"It's not as simple as that. Or easy."

"No, it is not."

Our unanimity having thus reached a point where words were almost entirely superfluous, I boldly decided to express my wish to her and said:

"I want you to sleep with that man and tell me about yourself and him. It seems to me that you have neglected us, that you haven't really abandoned yourself with anyone for a long time, and you've not given me the chance to identify and feel liberated."

72

"Who are you talking about?"

"Kustaa Mauri Armfelt."

"Well, it's not just up to me."

"Do you mean he doesn't want you?"

"Of course I don't mean that. But he prepares for everything so carefully. He says he doesn't want to spoil things by being overhasty. And the dogs have to get used to me first. Oh yes, we've talked about it."

"Good God," I couldn't help interrupting, "talked about it!"

"Yes. He's like that. Different. Or so ordinary. It's almost as if he were courting. Or training. Anyway, it's been agreed on in principle."

"Good God," I repeated, leaning back with the shock in my rocking chair, and almost managing to get it into motion from the floor; I was supposed to rock every evening and try to press my legs against the floor as much as possible. "You hear anything if you only live long enough. This is beginning to sound more interesting. And what about you?"

"I'm attached to him," Tamara said solemnly.

Then, suddenly, like someone out of her mind, she hurled the hot-water bottle so that it smacked against the bed post and fell on the floor. It was an old one and opened easily, so I started the journey from the rocking chair to the bed to pick it up before it leaked on the carpet. Tamara had risen to a sitting position and was holding her head in her hands.

"Imagine getting stuck with someone like that, dog-crazy—he's even supposed to keep bees in the country. He's interested in everything else, it seems. If only someone would say something bad about him."

"Maybe he's impotent," I said, preparing myself for disappointment too.

I was restless around this time, my work went badly and Tamara was away for long periods. I knew that she was busy; a large number of the patients were sent on leave or completely discharged, often to conditions where they had no chance whatever of pulling through. She was unhappy over the lack of proper transitional jobs, and had some hard words to say about therapy that only makes people quiet and uncomplaining so they can be got off one's hands. She was called for an interview and told that she ought to reconsider her attitude and take a more positive approach to her work. She told me all this in passing, without any kind of emphasis, but I felt that it was on her mind. I noticed that she had been crying. Much as I am on my guard against political power, especially its shackling effect on people's creativity, I could not help thinking that in some cases politics might be the right means to get something done. I even went so far as to telephone one of my old acquaintances who is on the city council. He is one of those rare politicians with whom I condescend to speak. He himself answered the telephone, and remembered me from bygone days.

"How are things with you these days?" he asked.

"Just fine."

I told him that I still regarded him highly in spite of his political career, and said that I was approaching him as a voter. He may have been busy, but he did not show it, letting me speak without interrupting. It may even be that a little of what I said stayed in his mind. I explained that the psychically sick should receive disability compensation, although this was not at present the case. The city should arrange for them a quota of rentable dwellings and properly supervised jobs to which they could go when they left the hospital. I had made a note of all these points, as I myself did not have the faintest idea about the matter. I was only involved for the sake of someone else, and consequently it was easy for me to act.

"Quite," he said, "the matter pops up every now and again. At the moment, however, as far as dwellings are concerned taxi drivers have been put at the top of the priority list. There are more and more taxi drivers coming to town all the time, and their families get broken up because there is no housing for them. These are big questions, tricky questions. Everything is tied up with something else. But I'll take the matter up after the summer vacation—this isn't really my baby, you know."

Tamara was cheered as if half the world were already turned upside down and waited on me hand and foot that evening, made me mint tea that was bitter and had been standing too long, and suddenly got the idea of walking me around for an hour in an antique wheeled affair of the kind supposed to be used in homes for the aged. It had been acquired at some time in the days of hope and faith, and had lain unused in a cupboard corner for years. I hoped that the colorado beetle or some other borer would have finished it off, but no, it was as bright and strong as ever when Tamara took it out.

"How can I forgive myself for forgetting this?" she said, pulling it out from behind clothes smelling of mothballs.

I tried to resist, but it was no use. As I shoved the apparatus across the room, battering the legs of the furniture and my own, getting it entangled in the carpet fringe and knocking over half a bottle of red wine from the draining board, while Tamara searched in the cupboard for lubricating oil to stop the wheels squeaking, I silently vowed that this would be the last time I'd ever get mixed up in politics; it caused nothing but trouble.

One evening Tamara brought with her a young woman who was supposed to leave for her home district the next day.

"What did you say the name of the place was?"

"Tyyskä."

She had big eyes that appeared to be permanently wide open. She would have looked just right on the cover of a smart fashion magazine, in angular attitudes, her eyes black-lined. She was supposed to have received a form entitling her to a daily allowance, but the doctor had already left when she went for it. So she had to stay somewhere overnight in order to get the form the next day. Tamara mercilessly left us together and started doing something in another room, though she knew well that I hated such forced social situations; nowadays I was quite entitled to avoid everything repugnant. But I am so slow to escape that I felt it best not to try, and so we sat in the same room without saying a word, both of us paralyzed. But after a while she began to speak, perhaps encouraged by my helplessness. And to my surprise there was a consoling note in her voice, as if she wanted me to be glad that I didn't have the same difficulties she had.

"I came here six months ago because I couldn't be alone," she explained. "I couldn't be with people either, because I was afraid all the time they would reject me. I lived in constant fear of being rejected. I fell in love with people on the bus, and when they got off at the next stop I felt they were tired of me and that was why they were leaving. I wanted to protect myself, and so I didn't dare to be with people or to be alone. Now I don't think I'm afraid to be alone. Today I felt for a moment that the doctor had left purposely so I would be without the right forms, but it didn't last long. So perhaps I'll get used to people bit by bit and not fall in love with them anymore."

I cleared my throat and tried to think of something to say to her. Should I congratulate her on her recovery and on getting over her love for people and finding the courage to manage on her own, or should I say something general about how people always need each other in the final analysis? I felt that she had already heard enough such clichés, and moreover had experienced their validity, the most fundamental of all humiliations. But evidently she did not expect me to speak; perhaps she imagined that besides being a cripple I was dumb, and found this both appealing and encouraging, or perhaps all the time she had been here she had not yet had the opportunity to express herself. In any case, she went on with increasing boldness:

"I've been thinking that attachment is an unnecessary lock on the mind. I feel as if I'd been bolted in, like when the hook on the outhouse door sometimes got fastened by mistake, and you couldn't get it open from the inside. It was a horrible feeling. You shake it and shake it but it just stays shut, till someone happens to pass by and undoes the lock. I asked them in the hospital to hypnotize me so I wouldn't get attached to people anymore. They could have just said: 'You are not attached to anyone, you'll never again become attached to anyone.' I believe it would help if the basic tendency were relieved. In hypnosis they get down to those deep levels from which everything comes."

"And did they agree to do it?" I asked, without thinking that by speaking I might shatter her illusion of the ideal listener. But she seemed to feel it was quite in order for me to speak at this point.

"In principle they'd have agreed to it, but there are very

77

few doctors who use hypnosis. There's a long waiting list. And my case wasn't considered so serious."

"The idea seems good," I said, surprising myself with the readiness with which I hastened to accept this notion. So this is what I too wanted, this is what we wanted: freedom from our neighbors and our feelings, those slight shreds of attachment that still bound us to each other, interfering with our final alienation; were we so hopeless? "The idea is interesting. This tendency to attachment is built into us biologically," I explained omnisciently, like a professor of wisdom, to give myself time to think. "The duckling becomes automatically attached to the first thing it sees. It might be possible to remove this propensity by doing something to its genes."

"Or by hypnosis," the girl insisted.

"As far as I know only the higher beings can be hypnotized."

"Oh yes," said the girl as if thinking aloud, "man is a higher being."

"Do you believe then, Miss . . ." I began, but suddenly felt a strong urge to call her by her first name: people who talk about such things should be more intimate with each other. Would she mind if . . . ?

"No, of course not. My name is Mirja."

"You can call me uncle. Uncle Lollipop if you like." She smiled and I went on:

"Do you believe, Mirja, that it is useless to hope that people will fulfill each other's expectations? Can't you imagine that people might answer each other's need for love with love, that life might open up, people be freed from their complexes, begin to value love and the emotional life as they now value property or art or health—as a standard-of-living symbol so to speak?"

She seemed to be thinking hard. It was as if her new philosophy, on which she had evidently intended to build her future life, was not very pleased with my flimsy, hastily constructed counterproposal. The thought passed through my mind that perhaps I was wrong to disturb the fabric of her thoughts just at the moment of returning home.

"Well," she said doubtfully. "Love is a constant state of readiness. It demands strength—strong people. It ties up energy. It's like, like . . ."

She did not find a substitute comparison. "Gives up trying for fear of failing." That was the sort of sentence in their reports, a sentence that followed them wherever they went or whatever they tried, only the thumbprints at the corners of the pages increasing, the folds becoming sharper.

"People are weak, timid, uncertain, frightened, sick," she said, glancing at my legs and speaking all the time in such a soft voice that it was surprising that it went on; as if she did not have the tiny bit of extra strength needed to raise her voice. "How can people like that manage to love, at least in this world?"

I suddenly felt that there were a thousand things I would have liked to ask her. I wanted them to go right through her brain and I wanted to listen to what it said. I snatched at the uppermost and said hurriedly:

"But what about man's aggressiveness? It seems to me our problem is aggressiveness."

"So it is," she said. "It comes from fear. And anxiety."

Tamara came into the room, fussy as a housewife. She had prepared sandwiches and wheeled them in on some kind of a trolley (how I hate anything that resembles a wheelchair). And when she came in I experienced something strange, something I would never have believed I would experience in connection with Tamara. I suddenly felt she was unwanted in the room, that she disturbed us. It was a long time since I had been interested in any outside person and his feelings. I did not like our being interrupted, even on the pretext of eating.

Tamara managed to fuss about for no apparent reason, so that at times she seemed to be in many places at the same time, and when I thought she had at last quieted down enough to sit in her chair, and I was about to start the discussion again, she began emptying an ashtray in the fireplace. I was forced to take a sandwich, one of those that is awkward to eat, with a bit of cucumber like a sail, and was about to ask—as part of it slid down my trousers to the floor—whether perhaps part of the day's program was picking up slices of cucumber from the floor with one's toes. Then I noticed that the girl was hungry and was eating up her sandwich with a healthy appetite. I began to like her more and more. Tamara poured tea into the cups.

"Darjeeling," she said as she handed me my cup, but for some reason I didn't give a damn just then whether the tea was from the Himalayas, the Caucasus, or the bottomless pit itself.

"What do you do for a living?" I asked as soon as my sandwich permitted me to speak.

"I'm a weaver," the girl said. "I used to look after the local library, which was open twice a week, but of course I won't get that job again, because I didn't let people out one evening."

"Why didn't you let them out?"

"Because I wanted to keep them near me. I felt I loved them all. And I was sure I could get them to understand."

The girl laughed at her former self that had loved so much and said: "Can I have another sandwich please? I'm terribly hungry. There was only soup there for lunch and it's not enough to keep me going for long—nerves use up so much."

"What do you weave?" I asked.

"Rugs."

"Can you live on that?"

"Well, from now on I'll have to live on it. I've been thinking that in the future I'll weave a message in each one of them. Up to now I've only put a message in some, but now I'll start to put one in all of them. There's always somebody who'll understand. Last summer there was a man from Ontario who came and said: 'I saw one of your rugs and

80

from that moment I've wanted to get one like it.' I said that I never weave two just the same, but that I'd make him an even nicer one. And I put a message in that one too. I'm beginning to know what kind of message will bring what kind of person. I've even sent a message to Australia. Maybe I'll weave night and day this summer. Once you've started there shouldn't be any interruptions—you shouldn't even talk to anyone. I've done a lot of designing while I've been here, especially after I stopped loving people."

"But you want them to come to see you all the same?"

"Oh yes, those that understand. And the others don't come anyway."

"Well, that's clear enough," I said, without looking at Tamara.

"Yes, as long as you can keep the different worlds apart. But borderline cases are always difficult. Sometimes some people understand a bit, but not altogether. You ought to help them, but they are always restless—they just can't relax. A little understanding only confuses them, but they aren't the ones to go through the whole of understanding. They stop at the beginning, or halfway, and only cause unrest."

"Can't you weave your messages so that only those understand who have understanding," I said, not letting Tamara's silence disturb our conversation.

"You can't do it," Mirja said, shaking her head. "Understanding is like being drunk, you get dependent on it, and you can see quite clearly that people always take the most difficult road to it. But that's the way total understanding is achieved. Can I have that last sandwich please?"

"Of course," Tamara said.

I felt a need to reflect for a long time, with nobody to disturb me. What right have we to exclude other people's imaginary worlds? Who has decided that of all possible worlds ours is the truest and most valuable, with all its violence and dominance of ideologies? Supposing at the very dawn of history humanity had made the wrong choice by allowing the active and the matter-of-fact to gain the upper hand over dreamers and casual ones. Supposing the really decisive struggle was fought in the mind, and the cruellest have won that too. And what if the reign of dreams is still to come? Dreams are delicate but tenacious, they are preserved like tortoises within their hard shells, they multiply like insects and protozoans, the world's most enduring species of all.

Tamara interrupted my thoughts by starting to talk about sleeping and bedclothes. It is odd that as soon as three people are under one roof, especially overnight, they begin to form some sort of community and for each a position and task takes shape, even if only temporarily. We were now quite obviously becoming Tamara's family, in spite of the fact that the house was mine, that she practically never took part in my household affairs (and I'd never have put up with it), that she did not know, for example, anything at all about my supply of linen. It was as if she had decided that we were together and liked each other. We were all beginning to get tired, in the way that I remembered from the rare occasions when there had previously been guests. Tamara mentioned a red bedspread, but for the life of me I couldn't remember where it was, so Mirja had to be content with an old quilt. She took hold of it and sniffed at it.

"People who were strangers to each other have slept under this," she said.

"Quite correct," I said. "How did you know?"

She reflected for a moment with eyes closed, the quilt in her hands.

"There's a level at which people know and understand," she said at length.

She looked sleepy, but her big eyes still looked as if, having been set open, they did not know how to shut. I could not resist asking her one more question: "Can one use that level just like that?" I said, feeling now that I was clearly one of those who understand a little, become restless, but are not capable of going through the whole of understanding.

82

"No, of course not," she said, "but this evening we have used it."

It was as simple as that. She went to the next room and the night light that Tamara had switched on illuminated her for a moment in the doorway so that she appeared transparent as a spirit, her fair hair breaking up the outline of the head. I recalled the old tale of how some souls, tired of humanity, refuse reincarnation and become ghosts because they can no longer accept any state, alive or dead.

I went through my usual evening routine, washed myself, used the catheter, aired the room. I had that rare feeling that comes when one has been with strangers after a long period. One feels good from the contact and yet disturbed. Sad to be left alone and yet waiting for it. For a moment I imagined the situation if the girl and I were left alone in the house. I was surprised that the idea excited me so much. Perhaps she would be quite different from Tamara. She might like the caresses of fingers and mouth. Perhaps she was physically different, anatomically ethereal. I had lost touch with other women, was forgetting what a woman feels like.

The idea pierced me sharply, as it had not done for years. And then for the first time for ages I felt a need for security and continuity, perhaps the same need that had kept Tamara with me, Tamara who constantly exposes herself to disturbances like this and worse. Suddenly I felt an intense gratitude toward her, the kind that overwhelms an old married couple like a fever and causes them to envelop each other in tender and solicitous thoughts. I began to miss her, as though I had not seen her for a long time, had neglected her.

When Tamara came and began to undress on the other side of the wide double bed, I looked at her with new eyes. The presence of a strange woman in the house, where we were normally alone, made our being together seem different. Suddenly our happening to be in the same room seemed more significant than before. I noticed that there were pleated shoulder straps on her brassiere. They were significant too. I leaned over to her side of the bed and pulled her toward me; I have strong arms. I said twice: "Wife. My wife."

I can't really remember what happened next, but it seemed that the girl appeared at some point in the doorway and said: "I don't know whether this is normal or abnormal, but it seems wrong to me that I have to sleep alone, when you two sleep together and keep each other warm." She had the old quilt wrapped around her. And Tamara answered: "Come over here on his other side." And the girl came, and let the old quilt fall on the floor beside the bed, and she had nothing on underneath it. "How do you caress a man?" the girl asked. "I don't know because I was married to a man who was ticklish and was always ready. He couldn't stand love, nobody can stand it." "You can practice with him," Tamara said, "but don't be disheartened with the result." And at some point their hands met on me. And I felt that I could move and that I moved in them, both of them in turn, and that the girl was different from Tamara, and that I tasted them and let them taste me, and that I no longer knew which one I sought, I wanted both of them, and at one point I asked how many a person can really love, and Tamara answered: "Four at least," and finally I felt clearly that I wanted to enjoy the girl because she was new and would go away. But Tamara had been and always would be in me. It was wonderful to be free from her for a moment, and for a few wing beats I was completely free.

I often intended to ask Tamara whether this really happened, but the moment when it would be natural never came, and so I always put it off.

In the morning they had both disappeared, and I was afraid that even Tamara was only a fantasy.

B ut she was not.

"That man's going to torture the life out of me before he's finished," she said, throwing herself into my best armchair without taking her coat off; it was old, it is true, and needed new upholstery. It had been the subject of many discussions with Tamara.

"You didn't bring any fabric patterns of course," I said.

"I can't stand it, I can't stand it any longer, it's tearing my nerves to shreds, it'll break me up," she lamented, waving her hands about and holding her head. She would certainly have thrown it into the corner if it had been possible.

I wanted to prolong this precious moment of revealment and make sure that the matter was not dismissed after a few emotional exclamations. So I said that green was perhaps after all a little too cold a color for this rather chill-looking room, overshadowed as it was by trees, and that I had come to the conclusion that some shade of red would be more suitable, perhaps brick red—or a sort of brownish grayish orange.

"Can't you hear, have you lost your hearing too?" she shouted with her eyes shut, and I gradually pretended to believe that she was really serious.

"What is it now? One of your lame ducks? New problems of rehabilitation?"

"Don't," she said. "Don't. Don't. You know all right."

The idea crossed my mind that my wild dream of a successful sadomasochistic relationship had finally come true for Tamara, and that I would enjoy this tremendous new experience while at the same time I could observe it analytically—this for me being the psychophysical peak of sexual sensation. Who would have dreamed that Kustaa Mauri had such depths? Surely Fate itself had led him to cross our path.

"Is he violent?" I asked cautiously.

"Violent," Tamara gasped. "If you only knew . . ."

She twisted in her chair. I asked whether it was difficult for her to sit, could I help her get undressed and go to bed—it was late and anyway we always talked things over in bed.

She did not resist. While I was undressing her I looked surreptitiously to see whether there were signs of biting, pinching, sucking, or scratching on her. I examined her armpits, her breasts, buttocks, and groin, but I could not discern anything besides what I had done myself (two wild-boar bites on the shoulder) and a couple of new moles that had appeared below the ribs, as they tend to appear when a woman grows older. As a matter of fact I have always wondered how people manage to refrain from snapping and pecking at each other. Middle-aged people should be covered with the scars of love; their bodies should be like a guest book, and bring back memories on lonely nights. The guides to lovemaking say that nothing excites a man and arouses his admiration so much as a half-moon or a hare's leap around the nipples made by a former lover, and even strong feelings

86

will tend to weaken unless there are nailprints to remind a man of the trails of love.

Well, I thought after my vain search, perhaps he only goes in for soundings that do no more than give goose flesh but leave no permanent traces, or secret bites that vanish within a few hours.

Tamara twisted and fretted in bed, throwing the covers off and complaining that the room was too hot. A moment later she was shivering and burrowed under the blankets, her teeth chattering. I tried to feel her forehead to discover whether she had a temperature.

"Keep away, don't come near me," she said. "I can't stand you any longer."

I was sure now that she was not herself.

"You're ill. Shall I call a doctor?"

"No, I can't stand anyone messing around with me now."

"You are ill."

"So I am, I've been taken ill, and no wonder."

"And he is the cause of all this?"

"Yes."

"My condolences," I said, as respectfully as I could.

Tamara sat up in bed with her hair in her eyes. She looked delirious. "I can't stand you any longer."

It was only now that the philologist in me realized what she meant by "you."

"Why include me?" I said innocently, though I remembered in the next moment that it was I who had longed to identify.

"You're both the same. Two of a kind"—she stopped to look for sufficiently strong words and in that instant I realized how an expression may be both too cruel and too mild—"is too much in one woman's life. What's the matter with you? Or is it my fault? Why do I get stuck with people like you? I haven't been with a real man since heaven knows when. I'm beginning to forget what a man is like. I'll soon start believing it's a lot of bunk. Existing just for the sake of appearances. Ornamental. And I wanted an ordinary man, a straightforward performer, steady and trustworthy like an organ pumper."

"Maybe," I said, mouth dry and forced to swallow, "it's only temporary."

"It isn't. He's proud of it. He says his self-respect isn't affected by things like that."

"What a goat," I said. "The biggest one of all."

Tamara threw herself back on the bed and banged her head into the pillow, as is her habit at moments of extreme anguish—no doubt she did this as a child. I wanted to remind her that this might easily cause a nosebleed, but couldn't make myself heard.

"I try to understand," she said, "I try, I try, I try to understand."

"Is it necessary?" I said. "Why should it be necessary?"

"Don't you realize, why don't you realize?" she said as if she were about to burst. "He means to me what I mean to you. I don't think I've been in love like this for heaven knows how long."

At the same moment a capillary in her nose broke and the blood burst out on the pillow. I started to fuss about, lumbering back and forth in the room, swinging myself without embarrassment from one piece of furniture to another, imagining myself an ape-man in the rain forests, not caring about anything, and to my surprise I moved more easily and quickly than usual. In a few moments I had found ice, a cold towel, and alum to stop the bleeding.

"And what about him?" I asked when Tamara was sitting, leaning against the end of the bed and holding the blood-stained towel to her face.

"I'm the first one he wanted to succeed with. He never before considered it worth all the fuss."

"Is that possible?"

"Yes. Anything is possible. Even coincidences that seem invented by a madman."

"And me here thinking that I had exclusive rights in that field."

"Now you see you haven't."

I had to stop and think. Something, I didn't know exactly what, was upsetting my ideas, my whole outlook on life, which in spite of everything I did have. I found myself remembering what Mirja had said about getting locked up by attachment, the difficulty it causes. And suddenly I couldn't resist asking:

"Why did you bring Mirja here? You had some reason for it."

"It's good for you to meet other people sometimes. And I thought she was the type of person you'd like. And I was right."

"You thought that we would become fond of each other?"

"That too."

"And that you would be set free?"

"Please don't give me up now," she said. "I need you."

I can't say how I felt. Was I in control of the situation or not? Was I winning at the moment or had I already lost everything?

"And what about him?" I said for the second time. "Does he want you with him?"

"Certainly not. After all, he's married, and we've agreed that this mustn't be allowed to upset his marriage in any way. Anyway I would side with the wife."

My feelings began to clear as after a shock, and I suddenly felt great sympathy for her, forgetting myself entirely. I thought about her earlier life, the little I knew about it, how she had always bruised herself in her collisions with people, exposed herself, put her expectations at a minimum and yet managed to be disappointed.

"Truly I would have wished you an ordinary man who was

free," I said, like a faithful old aunt who once again observes the sad truth of ancient wisdom.

"There aren't any like that," Tamara answered. "Men are either married or gone to the dogs, they either live at home or in a lousy lodging house. Free men are practically non-existent, and many of them are homosexuals. Oh yes, I've gone over the field in my mind. One day I took a man from the street to the hospital. He was drunk on meth and had been beaten up or hurt himself so he was all bloody. People who saw us laughed and said: 'You've got yourself a man there, miss—there's a man for you, miss.' And only a few weeks ago I took another one to hospital because he was haunted in the streets by big green dogs and his former wife was always shouting for help around the next corner. I suspect that's the man who's always ringing up and asking what color panties I've got on. I've gone through the whole spectrum."

She began to brighten up; other people's wretchedness tends to make us pull ourselves together.

I wanted to say something encouraging, and I said—with inexcusable frivolity when I come to think of it:

"You'll manage all right."

But Tamara seemed to take it at once as true, as if she had been waiting for me to say those very words. She looked me straight in the eye, and a smile hovered on her lips.

I felt that the faithful-aunt act should be played to the end, so I decided to improve my phrase a little and patted the convalescent on the shoulder:

"You'll certainly manage all right."

When she had quieted down and I had swung back and forth in my rocking chair for some time, presumably looking wiser than I was, I could not resist asking further questions, first of myself, then, little by little and cautiously, of Tamara:

"Could you explain why you were so upset?"

And in answer I was given a lot of confused, contradictory

information which, only after considerable formulation, could be organized into some sort of whole.

A situation or occasion had been arranged, the one "there had been talk about," which had been "agreed on in principle" and awaited only practical implementation. They had driven in a car.

"Where?" I asked.

"Oh, what does that matter? Finland is full of places like that. Imagine the kind of surroundings you want to."

"It's not that easy. I always need some small visual details before the scene becomes familiar to me and starts to live. After that I can move around in it without trouble—it creates itself before my eyes."

"There were drooping birches in the yard. The local people call their branches lambs' tails. They were in front of the house and in front of the room where we were. And nearby there was a farmhouse—the wife was getting the calves used to being outside. They'd been born in March, in late winter, and they'd never seen summer or the outside world. And they were afraid of it. They didn't even know they could jump, they were surprised and frightened by their own movements and bumped into each other. And then they didn't realize the trees were solid and wouldn't budge, and they ran straight into them."

"Perhaps they were blind."

"No, they weren't, they had lovely black-rimmed eyes and they looked straight at you. The farmer's wife had to be in the pen with them till they got used to freedom, you could see they looked to her for security. I talked to her and she told me how the cows got homesick. The first day they were put out in the woods to pasture the young ones especially got so homesick they just walked back and forth close to the fence and mooed toward home. They stamp a path by the fence nearest home. The summer before there had been a Friesian bull in the herd, and some of the calves are black and white,

91

some of them brown. Friesian bulls are much gentler than Finnish ones, she told me."

"Really," I said, having had my fill of the environmental details. "So there was a motel by the farmhouse, or were you in a camping ground?"

"Don't use those horrible words 'motel' and 'camping ground.' I'm allergic to the very idea of them. I still want to tell you about the calves, that they don't chew grass, they suck it. And one young cow had had a calf too early; it will always be weaker than the others."

"Very interesting. Your knowledge of the world has greatly expanded since last we met."

"So it has."

"And what about the room?" I asked.

"I don't remember anything about the room. Only that there were two beds in it. One of them squeaked, the other one didn't."

"Which one did you choose?"

"The one that didn't squeak of course."

"Fools. You missed a great deal. You should have thought of me."

"I'm sorry, but I really didn't think of you at that moment. And in general I can say that the less I think of you then, the more I have to tell you afterward."

"True," I said. "I understand. Go on."

"I had the curse."

"Well, that's not exactly the end of the world."

"That's what he said."

"Imagine. We will give him points for that."

"Don't be so horribly calculating. This isn't a game of rummy."

"Don't get upset. Easy does it. What happened then?"

Tamara raised a hand to her eyes. Telling quite clearly exhausted her. On the other hand this must be good for her; people love to talk about their pains.

"Nothing."

"Don't jump right to the main point. Something must have happened. For example, did he wash or rub himself down with a cold towel or do exercises?"

"I don't remember anything like that."

"I suspect you kept your eyes shut," I said, quite worked up now. "Eyes should be kept open, always and in all situations. That way you learn a great deal. What sort of size was he?"

"Don't. I don't remember and I don't want to remember."

But I decided to be ruthless, as always when I have reached this point.

"Surely you looked at him and felt him, found out about him. I told you that if a man does not, figuratively speaking, leap on top of you at once, and show he wants to take the reins in his hands, one must examine him and determine from the state he is in what measures should be taken. Didn't you remember that?"

"Yes, I remembered."

"Well. What was it like? Even if it's only a couple of inches long in the rest position, that's no catastrophe."

"It was sort of wrinkled and flat, like a rosette—smaller than yours. I've never seen anything like it."

"But didn't it . . . ?" In my impatience, unable to find words quickly enough, I made a descriptive movement with my hand.

"No. It didn't change at all, it just seemed to crumple up more. Oh, I did all I'd learned with you and a bit more. But those tricks didn't work with you either."

"I am a special case. The day when electrodes can be fitted in place of the erectile center, my problem can be crossed off the list."

"It may be the same with him."

"It's not as simple as that. The trouble may be in the head or in the whole personality. From what I know about him I'd tend toward the latter diagnosis. But what happened then?"

"We caressed each other and kissed each other and I felt

I loved him anyway. Of all the men I know I would have chosen him."

"And you told him that?"

"Of course. I allow myself that. If I like someone, I show it—he can do what he likes with the knowledge. I'm too old to pretend in things like that."

I had to think again. I was not yet clear what feeling would be foremost in me, and what state of mind I'd find myself in. Would curiosity and interest prevail, or would I sink into depression because this encounter from which I had expected so much, for which I'd been living all spring, had proved to be such a crushing disappointment?

After taking stock of my ideas, my possibilities, and my resources, it clearly became necessary to discover for a start how much hope was still left. Secondly, I did not at this stage fully understand the reason for Tamara's acute shock.

"Actually I surpassed myself many times over," she said. "Sometimes I've been quite helpless in a similar situation, or I haven't liked the person enough to take the trouble. And I've always felt shy. Now I started to feel I was torturing him. I remembered how Mirja complained about her ignorance, and I suddenly felt I didn't know anything either. You can hardly think of a ghastlier situation than getting out of a bed with dignity where nothing's happened."

"Come now," I said, with the support of all my experience in the field, the cock in the chicken coop, "surely something must have happened there."

Tamara looked at me.

"Sometimes it seems to me you really don't understand anything at all."

"And what about him?" I asked for the third time.

"He told me I mustn't think he liked me any the less because of it."

"How romantic. This might lead to a platonic affair."

"No," Tamara shrieked, "no, I can't stand any more

platonic affairs. I'm already quite . . . If only you knew how it feels!"

I regret to say that I could not resist a peal of laughter at this profound moment when, for the first time, we really understood each other. At first she did not even understand what I was laughing about, but started to look hurt. Then she realized.

"I'm sorry."

"Not at all," I said, unable to stop laughing even for her sake, "not at all, this is delightful . . . ha ha ha, just carry on, don't let my hilarity disturb you, I haven't enjoyed myself so much for ages."

Did Prometheus really laugh while the vulture was tearing out his liver, or did I make that up? I am sure that he laughed; that was when the sense of humor was born. I believe he screamed with laughter at both gods and vulture; no doubt it alarmed the vulture and bits of liver went down the wrong way. And Tantalus must have tittered whenever the water receded.

"It's all very well for you to laugh," said Tamara, immediately realizing that these righteous words were the wrong ones too; everything ordinary is out of place between us. The laughter infected her too and I could feel her relief. But at the same time tears began to gather in her eyes of their own will. At first they stayed in the corners, making her eyes look larger than normal, and she kept them open as if remembering my exhortation that eyes should be kept open in all circumstances. Then she came, eyes brimming over, and put her head on my knees as was her habit, her hair spreading over my lap. The bloodstained towel was forgotten in her left hand. Her body shook with sobs.

"Please don't ask why I'm crying."

Why should I ask a thing like that?

*L*eaving for the country was not, to tell the truth, a very soul-inspiring affair. I did realize in the midst of all the confusion why I shun moving. Whenever I stir I feel as if I were constantly bumping into walls or trees, like the calves Tamara described. It seems as if my own limitations were external obstacles against which I batter myself. After much displacement my self-assurance is at a low ebb for days, as if it were hiding. It needs a long period of silence before it is willing to come forth again. But at such times I am strongly aware that I exist; my limitations remind me of it.

This is a painful and contradictory state. I am interested in psychasthenia, the weakening of the sense of self and the great oppression caused by it. Several of Tamara's patients suffer from it, and I have tried to get her to tell me about specific cases, but she feels bound by professional silence and is unwilling to describe anything more than general symptoms and patterns of behavior such as may easily be found in books. She claims to suffer from it herself from time to time, and at such times she takes refuge in me. However, she claims that she doesn't even "feel" my presence then, she only "knows" it, even if I am in the same room. It may last for days. When it ends, she says that she starts to "see" again.

I believe that the move gave rise to a similar state in me, and I came to think that change may cause it too. Perhaps we all suffer from a weakening of the sense of self as a result of the constant changes imposed on us by the modern world. In connection with our departure a series of complex movements were expected of me, and nobody remembered that I was not fit to do them. I was put in humiliating situations. Since then I've often dreamed that baskets of breakable utensils are thrust into my hands, and cardboard boxes whose cords bite into my fingers, and on top of all that I am urged to hurry up so the truck would not block the road too long.

I complained about this to Tamara, but she treated the matter with complete indifference.

"Life will repay you," she said, and even laughed. "It's funny but it really does seem to give back the same measure. You once caused me such terror that I still wander in my dreams through the university corridors—they're all dark for some reason—or in the library, searching frantically for some work from the time of Habakkuk in which I have to count all the infinitives; or else I'm tormented by the feeling that I'd never understand the examination requirements because they're so complicated. After dreams like that it's a real pleasure to wake up to this life—so they're of some use. Someday I'll wake up relieved that I'm old and that it will soon all be over and done with."

I was ostentatiously silent, but I don't think she even noticed.

My legs seemed to hurt as if from too much walking, though in fact I'd mostly used my hands, arms, shoulders, and armpits. It is evident that in moving with the help of my hands I also created a kind of tension in my legs. So tension can exist even in paralyzed muscles and nerves, as if

97

the power to suffer is the most lasting of the sensory perceptions.

The villa we had rented was a reasonable distance from the city, and in a beautiful spot, although I was too irritated to admit it. Tamara expected me to continually praise the place, because she had discovered it in a mass of "quite impossible," "awful," and "hopeless" places. But I had not the slightest intention to laud it—or to praise Tamara herself —for as long as my uneasy dreams spoiled my nights. The place was owned by numerous heirs to whom it had been left by a childless couple; they were so at odds with one another that they couldn't even reach unanimity on the sale price, for which reason the house had been empty for more than a year. They were all well-off people, lawyers, dentists, professors, and pharmacists, but they quarreled like stray dogs over a carcass about this property which had so unexpectedly fallen into their hands.

The house was furnished, and abundantly. Old clothes still hung in the cupboards. In one drawer of a bureau there was a pile of used corsets as if awaiting the day when they would all be washed. In the bedroom cupboard there were five old-fashioned handbags and a drawerful of shoes; the secret of property is obviously accumulation. The valuables had already been divided; these were articles that had not been good enough for anyone. On the walls light patches showed where pictures had been hung; bright wallpaper patterns near the floor spoke of a vanished sofa. But pieces of furniture still remained in superfluity, always within arm's reach of one another—perhaps Tamara had arranged them a little. Curved french windows, of the kind that once belonged to the dwellings of all better-class families, gave on to a slope leading down to the lake. On one side the slope became rock, on the other a swampy water meadow. Beyond could be seen a farmhouse.

Tamara was as enthusiastic as if she had created all this in six days and brought me to see it on the seventh. She would have liked to drag me off right away to examine the yard buildings and the sauna, but I said I'd save some exploring for next week and politely declined. She went alone and returned with an armful of books.

"The *aitta* is full of trashy novels," she said. "The dreams of childhood always come true too late, but they do come true. I hope there's some erotic literature too. As a child I thought novels were only about sex life, like medical books, and that's why they were forbidden to children. It was a terrible disappointment to discover that people kept away from each other in books too and seldom made love, and that the medical book was full of illnesses—there were only a few pages about sex and they'd been torn out in the library."

"Dear, dear," I said, brightening up a little. "Let's hope that now you'll find some compensation for those disappointments. Who knows how they amused themselves, that odd couple."

"I could dress up in those clothes this evening and pretend I was lost in the house," Tamara said. "And then I'd suddenly find you."

But for the first time for a long period I didn't feel like playing. Perhaps I was too alienated by the environment, perhaps I wondered vaguely what would happen if I were left here alone and did not enjoy it. Perhaps I am more dependent both on environment and on my preferences than most people. Without beauty I cannot live. Without attachment my life seems completely groundless. I must begin to like this place and feel its significance, like my overgrown garden, my shady aspens, and the polygonum growing in the cracks of the steps, which I remembered now. Everything here was excellent and interesting, but for some reason I had not yet gained contact with nature. That was it, I thought, in the country one must have contact with nature, otherwise everything remains alien and one feels that one is an alien oneself, like an unacclimatized plant moved from somewhere else, like myself now.

99

On the fourth night I had a dream that I was walking with Tamara through a swampy water meadow that gave way underfoot like the muddy bottom of my dream lake. I remember clearly that this dream was in color, and at the same time as I took part in it I observed myself from the outside. Tamara was wearing a long black coat buttoned up to the neck, like one that had been hanging on a nail in the cupboard, and a wide-brimmed hat decorated with a chimney sweep's brush. She had trouble walking in her long skirts, and they became heavy with everything that caught in them. But I lifted my legs lightly. And she put her arm around my waist and suddenly she had her arm around Kustaa Mauri and we three walked together and he and I lifted her up over ditches. And then Tamara said: "I can't go on in these heavy old clothes," and she laid herself down in the long grass and we began to extricate her from the black coat, we kissed her and busied ourselves with the buttons. But then everything changed as it does in a dream, and Tamara and Kustaa Mauri began to busy themselves over me as if they were eating cray-fish, and I did not mind at all. On the contrary, it felt as if armor had been taken off me and I sighed deeply with relief. Tamara said: "All that's locked must be unlocked, everything must be opened and released." And the lowest part of my stomach between my legs was heavy and cramped; something tried to get out. And when they got it out it stood up like a space rocket and around it there was a base like a vulva. It grew to gigantic proportions so that Tamara and Kustaa Mauri looked like ants as they bustled around it. I realized that this was the final concretization of our phallic cult, the greatest achievement of human thought in this sphere. Then it left its base and began to rise toward the stars and new planets that appeared on every side, toward quasars and the boundary of worlds, and it became smaller and smaller until I no longer saw it except through the eyes of my soul. With their help I followed its journey to the limit of existence where everything shatters. And suddenly in the middle of the dream I knew that Kustaa Mauri had been here and that they had found this place together, had gone around here to look at everything. At the same time the reality of the dream began to change to something else, as if the level had slowly turned over before my eyes to show its wrong side, and I returned with a feeling of slight distaste to my normal condition, limited by senses, abilities, time, and skin—Caliban's problem. Then I was completely awake and realized that Tamara was sleeping by my side.

But the dream atmosphere still predominated, and the dream itself seemed almost to continue. I felt strong and relaxed and began to caress her, figuring that it was time to wake up.

"Strange that I didn't notice those birches before—what is it they call those long hanging branches?"

"Lambs' tails," Tamara answered, half opening an eye.

My interest in nature was now awakened, and the landscape was familiar. I already had memories and dreams of it.

When we arrived it was dandelion time. The whole slope down to the lake, the foot of the rocks, and half of the water meadow were full of dandelions. The pollen gathered along the shore in a yellow streak, and the brook flowing through the meadow, which started from another lake on the other side of the road, was completely covered with a thick, undulating coat of pollen. One day I noticed that there were streaks of oil, and spent half a day lying flat on my stomach by the bridge, scooping up with a ladle the yellow, dark-streaked stuff from above some sunken logs, where it had stuck. The next day a similar float was there, though I had managed to clean the brook completely the day before. Then I noticed that the stuff had sunk to the bottom on the other side of the bridge and got caught in the bushy water plants which thus filtered the water so that what flowed into our lake was clear and clean-looking.

I moved around out of doors here more than usual, though indoors Tamara often carried me. It was as if nowadays she just didn't have the patience to wait for me to move from one place to another in my own way. It was easier to lift me up in her arms and set me down in the place where she happened to want me at that particular moment.

"D'you know," she said, pressing her hand on her heart, "when we came here, all my chest felt painful, especially around the heart. I couldn't have carried or lifted anything at all. Even lugging a bucket of water around took all my strength. Now I feel I could manage anything. My whole body had grown painful with stress during the winter. It's only by the skin of one's teeth that one manages to get through to the summer alive."

She became tanned, freckled, and peeled. I stripped great shreds of skin from her back. "Look, I cast my skin every summer, I renew myself completely." Her body was a pattern of brown and white areas, like a map of unexplored regions, an aerial photograph of untouched and unknown wildernesses, inviting the explorer. Her hair was straight and dragged tight at the nape of the neck, out of the way, fastened with some odd bit of wool. "One must have the right at least in summer to be ugly and unpleasant; I'll smile again in autumn," she said.

And although it was true that she hardly smiled here, her face had a relaxed look; even the permanent lines in her forehead seemed to smoothe over a little. And sometimes unknowingly she smiled. For example when she lifted a bucketful of water from the lake, full of the tiniest insects busily moving, only just visible to the eye. She carried the pail to me.

"Stardust in a bucket," she announced. "What on earth makes them group themselves like that? Who knows, perhaps they obey the same laws as the planets in the universe."

103

And true enough these almost microscopic little organisms, hundreds of thousands of them in the bucket, perhaps millions, grouped themselves as at the command of some invisible dancing master, now in one conglomeration in the middle of the bucket, now in a bridge stretching from one side to the other, like the Milky Way in space, and again in turn disturbed to become a flat disc, like Andromeda's spiral nebula, a galaxy at light-years' distance. After the bucket had been standing for some time on the table, they had all settled at the edge nearest the light from the window, and rippled there.

We examined frogs together too. It appeared that frogs do not all develop at the same time, as we had both thought, but in the middle of the summer one could still find some of very different ages and sizes. In the water meadow's stagnant muddy pools black tadpoles darted, while on the banks of the brook sprawled little creatures with tiny legs looking like the first living things in the universe having just discovered how to crawl onto the shore. On a hot day the big majestic toads dwelling on the bottom of damp paths were a real problem; they did not seem to give way to anything else in creation. Hobbling carefully past them I felt a strong desire to protect man, the poor decrepit being that mutilated himself spiritually and physically, and was dying amid the nature he had destroyed, expecting with his last breath sympathy from the animals he had almost completely wiped out. Could there be a more pitiable creature?

Another thing that bothered me was the insects. It seemed that this summer they were especially plentiful and of many species. I have never before, for example, seen so many long, flying, articulated whatever-they-are, with one red movable part in the middle of the body and long feelers. I especially abhor a combination of crawling and flying; it always makes me think that nature has sometimes been too eager in implementing her sadistic fantasies. There are also many creatures which nature has provided with so many legs that

104

they don't themselves seem to know what to do with them, not to mention those many other accessories with names unknown to me, such as long hairs coming out from behind, which, though they don't look especially attractive, may be indispensable to the creature in question.

Wasps tried to build nests on the ceilings of both the privy and the porch; in the places most used in fact. I could not—friend of nature though I am—approve their intentions. I fought for three days against the lodgers in the privy: I destroyed the bottom of the nest several times a day, I sprayed the place with acetone and deodorants, but always it reappeared in the same place. Not until I removed from the ceiling a structure resembling a ball of blotting paper, with some cells already in place, were the wasps convinced and no longer appeared. I thought I was merciful because at any rate I let them live, until I saw one of the others, which had planned to build on the porch ceiling, die of grief on the porch window. They had already managed a small globe when I deliberately poked it down with my stick. One wasp was inside and buzzed to the porch window. I offered it several chances to fly out and seek a better place to live, but it always came back, moved crazily around the place where the nest had been, and finally settled, immobile, on the window as if it were hatching an egg. I understood that it did not have the spirit to start all over again. It sulked on the window, wings spread, proboscis out, and day after day slipped farther down. I consoled myself by thinking that it no longer suffered, but imagined it was looking after its nest, fulfilling the purpose of its life. On the evening of the third day it had slipped down to the window sill, but was still alive, its wings opened as if trying with its last strength to save face. On the fourth day it died, teaching me an unforgettable lesson in the courage of its kind. And I glued its heroic body to the curtain in my room as a reminder of universal community, reinforced by suffering, and of the empathy which exists in spite of everything.

On top of all this, there was a constant rustling, thumping, and clicking in the house. At some point a great swarm of blue-green, shiny, long-horned beetles appeared, and in joy that their complex development had reached its end they flew, especially in the evening, from wall to wall. First one heard a humming, then a smack as an insect banged into the wall, then a thump as it fell on its back on the floor, and finally tremendous exertions as it tried with its dozen legs to turn the right way up on the slippery floor. This might go on for hours. Now and then they fell on the bed, and I suffered from a fear I had never before experienced, that they were walking quite undisturbed along my legs without my knowing anything about it, and after that I always had the feeling they were struggling through the jungle of my body hair. After a while they found rivals in the shape of big black beetles, whose peculiarity was to spend hours wandering between the ceiling boards until they fell down. They seemed to aim particularly for the bed. Killing big beetles is a butcher's job; they are in every way designed to make the process unpleasant; from inside them great quantities of colored entrails spurt out, and they take long to die, still struggling even after they are in pieces. One species revenged their death by smelling like a medicine chest. I was completely at their mercy, for I lacked the advantage of my species of being able to crush them on the floor with my feet.

Tamara slept, but I lay awake listening to the rustling and the next thump. If these insects eat wood, I thought, they will manage to demolish the house before the heirs have come to an agreement about the selling price. It was the only consolation I found in this situation.

Then a woodpecker chanced to become our neighbor. It's charming, Tamara exclaimed, when the bird appeared tapping away first here then there, and so tame. I had already tired of its voice, which was like a stifled scream, and its eternal hopping everywhere, when one morning it became apparent that it had nested in a hollow rowan at the foot of the rocks, a couple of feet from the ground. The baby woodpeckers began to shriek as soon as they got out of their shells, and they have gone on shrieking without stop since, night and day. Even Tamara has shown faint signs of irritation. For my part I have begun to feel sorry for the mother bird. It seems to me that she is thinner. She fusses about all the time, she even pecked at the flagpole many times, and her ears are always ringing with the ghastly din of her offspring—she never gets a moment's peace to catch a breath, as the country-folk say. One morning, true, I heard her ordering her brood to be silent, and it was so sharp an order that I was woken by it. It was as if the rocks had been hit with a hammer. I couldn't refrain from getting up and hobbling to the steps. It was a Sunday morning, beautiful and warm; the mother woodpecker screamed for her life and the chicks were quiet. I saw that a white and brown cat had appeared in the yard and was moving toward the rowan. And now I started to shout, swinging my crutches so that I nearly fell down the steps. Tamara woke up too and ran out in alarm. Holding her breasts, she rushed to chase the cat away at the last minute.

"Well, that does it," she said, flopping into a wicker chair on the veranda. "After this we won't have peace night or day. And I thought I'd be free here from taking care of things."

Since then we have listened to the noise of the young wood-peckers without cessation. If there is a break, even for a moment, we sharpen our hearing and are prepared to rush out helter-skelter, even I. Besides, we have studied the cries of the mother bird, coming from all sides of the house, and have learned to distinguish different nuances in her sounds as well as the chicks'. When the mother approaches the nest, the young scream as if they were being decapitated; when she is farther away they cheep more cautiously, but always heartbreakingly. With chill hearts we are already wondering how we shall endure the phase when they begin to come out of the nest, learn to fly, and fall to the ground, when this present stage is so unbearable. How will we stand listening to the mother's advice, the young ones' helpless wailing from branch and grass? He who has not had a woodpecker's nest as neighbor simply hasn't lived.

I've hardly had time to think about things erotic all this time, and the little thought I did give it was from the woodpecker's point of view. It doesn't seem to have had much joy for such a great squalling, or do birds couple many times during the spring? The swallows seem to take the business much more lightly, though they are always joyful, the incarnation of joy; the swallow's joy, the swallow is joy, joy is like a swallow—I play with the notion as I watch them streaming around the house, listen to the joyful frolic in the attic where they nest. Sometimes it seems they raise the roof as they dive back and forth beneath the eaves.

"Don't you feel that people are very unfruitful in the midst of all this?" I said to Tamara.

"In a way," she said. "Every summer I imagine I'm going to be pregnant."

"Really?" I said in surprise. This was something I had not known. "Even though you used to be so afraid of it, as you told me—counted the days on the calendar and suffered traumas?"

"That's quite different," she said. "The idea of conception is the most fascinating there is. That's what dominates in nature. That and continuity."

"Strange," she added, "continuity seems to require new combinations of individuals."

As I already mentioned, when we came it was dandelion time. The fields were yellow. The roadside was resplendent. For one who has not grown accustomed to it, it would have been an incredible sight. With the extinguishing of the dandelions, the white phase began. Cow parsley and the downy dandelion heads dominated the landscape. They surrounded the house like snowdrifts. (I've often wondered at people's delight in metaphors; there must be some deep psychological reason; by connecting things with one another, perhaps, man makes the world of his conceptions familiar and secure, explains to himself what he likes and why. And having thought this far, I realize that I want to say "like a cloud fallen to earth," because this comparison, for which there is no equivalent in my actual experience, brings back the whole fantasy world of my childhood, where everything was possible, fairy tales lived and I believed. Maybe we use metaphors to connect adult and childhood experiences. But this is something that nobody seems to have studied, and I have never assigned this subject to my students.)

The white cloud phase lasted almost two weeks, then a mass of blue flowers appeared, spreading bellflowers and vetch, and at the same time, in their special place in the open meadow, the buttercups, and in the compact grass tufts right by the water's edge, the densely twining cinquefoil.

It was as if I could notice only these obvious cycles in the landscape. I had to admit to myself that I was becoming inured to nature too, becoming indifferent to it as to so many other things before. Nor did I feel any regret. The only thing that mattered was that I was here with Tamara, that she was near me. Through her I could look at unknown worlds, the unattainable, as if I were watching the movements of nebulae through a powerful telescope.

Perhaps her thoughts had traveled the same orbit for, lying limp in the sun, small drops of perspiration shining on the bleached down of her upper lip, she suddenly said, stretching her hands high above her head:

"It would be wonderful to spend a hot day like this with a man, take everything he can give, and drink cold beer in between."

I felt myself becoming warmer at once, though I was sitting in the shade. Reality came rushing back toward me from light-years away, back onto this planet. Something began to shout inside me like a baby woodpecker in a tree.

"**W**hat would you think about him coming here now and then?"

"Kustaa Mauri?"

"Yes—after all this is no distance by car."

I needed to let the proposal revolve in my mind. I had no previous experience of such a situation, and the last thing I wanted was to spoil my chances by making an overhasty decision. Besides, there were more sides to the matter than appeared at first sight.

"How would you explain the setup here to him?"

"I've already told him how things really are—that you aren't good for anything. And that I'm just waiting to inherit from you—that explains everything."

"But does he believe that?"

"Oh, listen, that's nothing compared to what men invent about their wives. It really makes you wonder where the kids come from. Besides, at this stage a little guessing can only be

110

good. Uncertainty may excite him and stimulate a healthy aggression in him."

"Are you so sure about that?"

"I couldn't swear to it, but I've studied his psyche, even his way of moving and walking—that tells you a lot. And I've come to the conclusion that his sexual age is twelve—he hasn't even gone through his puberty properly. After all, most men reach the puberty stage and stay there. That's no problem in itself. Even a baby can get an erection."

Tamara was in form again. The country, sunshine, and carrying water had done her good. Her depression was wiped away: she had confidence in herself again. Nothing in fact disturbed our peace and quiet except the telephone; in spite of her horror of it she refused to disconnect it even here. Her answering service gave suicide candidates this number, which was still listed as "Summer Residence," like for the finest families. Telephone phobia has perverse features. While I was considering how I might be affected by the sight of Kustaa Mauri, and whether for example his appearance might prove an obstacle to my identifying with him, the phone rang to interrupt my thoughts. Tamara went to answer it and the following conversation ensued (elaborated by my intuitive gifts).

"Who is it that answers your phone and keeps repeating the same thing over and over again?" the person calling asked.

"That's my answering service. I'm in the country."

"Do you have two minutes' time?"

"Well, two minutes then." (From this I guessed what was coming next. These conversations always started like this and followed a pattern with which I too was familiar.)

"How are you?"

"I'm very well, thank you. How are you?"

"It's so difficult because I've got an erection all the time. Can you spare me those two minutes?"

111

"I've already promised," Tamara said, sighing barely audibly. Evidently the situation did not arouse very passionate feelings in her.

"Tell me what you're wearing."

"A brown blouse and brown shorts."

"A brown blouse and brown shorts. Tell me what color brassiere you have."

"Black."

"A black brassiere. I take it off now. You have beautiful breasts. I kiss them. They hang a bit, don't they?"

"Yes, they do."

"Never mind. I kiss your beautiful breasts. Tell me what color panties you have."

"They're black too."

"Are they lace?"

"Yes."

"Black lace panties. I take them off. You're naked now. You're beautiful. Tell me whether you have a big bush."

"Well, quite big."

"What color is it?"

"Brown."

"A big brown bush. Put your hand there."

"No. I have to ring off in a moment. The coffee's boiling over."

"Don't go yet. I need another moment. Tell me what color labia you have."

"I don't exactly know."

"Can't you have a look? Are they rose-pink?"

"No. They haven't been for a long time."

"They're dark like those of a mature woman, near black. I lick them. I drink your juice. I take you now, darling. I come in you. You're mine now."

"The coffee's boiling on the stove, I must ring off now."

"Thank you, darling, thank you."

"You're welcome. Keep well."

Tamara was always serious and upset for some time after a

112

call like this. Now she suddenly became tired and was no longer interested in continuing our recent conversation. I was thoughtless enough to say:

"Why don't you just put the phone down?"

She was angry.

"How can you say things like that? It might be someone who hasn't any opportunity for sex life. It might be an invalid."

Yes. Quite.

"Though I'm almost sure," she said, "that it's the man who was haunted in the street by huge green dogs and who fell in love with me on the way from Runeberg Street to Hesperia Hospital. Whenever he managed to get away from the dogs his wife started yelling for help around the corner, and when he ran to her rescue she had already moved around the next corner and was yelling there, and so it went. It was last September. I was coming from that seminar on Mental Health and Human Relations and standing at the bus stop wondering what I was really doing at a stupid academic occasion like that. This man appeared and spoke to each person standing at the bus stop, but nobody wanted to listen to him. I thought I'd listen at least. He wanted somebody to take him to the hospital, because it would be easier for him to get in. We started walking there together, and he explained that if he could get into the hospital and get proper treatment his life would be quite different for a couple of weeks—then everything would start afresh. I told him my name when he asked and he told me his, but I've forgotten it. We shook hands there in the hospital entrance and he said: 'I notice I'm in love.' When I walked away, I had the feeling that this was why I had put up with the whole stupid seminar, all the speeches, and been at the bus stop at that particular time. He was still quite young and even good-looking, only everything was so unhappy, sick, and inflamed. People who look like that are considered criminal, and are treated accordingly. They don't even have the basic right to speak to other people. Then if someone happens to speak to them as to an ordinary person, they're so happy that they fall in love."

"A moving tale," I said, hearing it probably for the fifteenth time. "And only one out of five thousand. What a pity I couldn't be your teacher in the field you finally chose. I'd have given you the task of making a study on the sex life of bums."

"Don't sneer, it's no laughing matter. It's one of the things that makes them feel worthless; they can't manage even that. Nonsatisfaction of a physical need is always spiritually humiliating—hunger to begin with. It's the hungry that bow and are ashamed, not the well-fed. Satisfaction and self-respect directly correspond with one another. In my view self-respect resides in the fingertips, the arse, the lips, and the tongue, those places where the nerve ends are thickest. That's why they are such sore, such sensitive, and such important regions."

This was a quite boringly familiar subject, threshed out endless times between us. I didn't even feel like identifying with the poor devil.

"I thought you had the coffee on. What's happened to it?"

She did in fact begin to make coffee, banging the coffee pot so hard against the draining board that the paint flaked off the wall. In the country we drink coffee, tea in town.

"I've always been honest with him," Tamara said. "I've respected him as a person. When I was wearing black panties I've said black, and if they were white I've said white. And I feel he's known that and appreciated it."

"But imagine what a change it would have been for him if you had said light blue, or orange, or rose-pink, no matter what they really were, or that they were embroidered with forget-me-nots or touch-me-nots. That might have pleased him even more. You could have used your intuition and chosen the color according to his mood."

Tamara stopped with the coffee pot in her hand, already a

little more relaxed. (It must be admitted that her telephone affairs tried our relationship a little.)

"You're hopeless, but you may be right. Or we're both right. Truth is a sum. It isn't what you say or what I say, but what we say together. Change is good of course. And imagination is another reality. But I'm tired of constant change."

" 'I am tired of change,' said the princess, 'give me monotony and the gray everyday.' That might make a clean story. Say you are not wearing any panties at all."

"I've said that already. I once happened to have just got out of the bath when he called."

"And what did he say then?"

"It seemed to me he was terribly disappointed. Undressing has its own purpose, it's a ritual, like Advent before Christmas. And in this eroticism by wire one must pay attention to evocative details just as much as when it's visual. Would you like some coffee?"

Thus we had slipped away from our subject, even though erotic reality stayed within close reach all the time. Tamara herself led us back to the focal point.

"You still haven't answered my question."

"And that was?"

"Do you mind if we meet here? It wouldn't necessarily mean that you had to be away then."

I noticed suddenly that the way she said "we" and "him" annoyed me tremendously, and the way she took it for granted that I knew what she meant by these pronouns. She didn't consider at all that I might have my own concept of "we," perhaps not the same as her own, but equally valid. I intended to say a few well-chosen words about this, but she didn't let me speak.

"I don't mean that I'd hide you in a cupboard, though there are plenty of them here and roomy ones too. But I'm sure things like this can be agreed on and talked over openly. People discuss their problems too little nowadays."

"You must bear in mind that I am unused to visual experiences," I said, swallowing my intended remark with my coffee. I tried to imagine how it would be if Kustaa Mauri were sitting there gulping coffee with us; I realized in the same instant that a meal, eating together, was so relaxing, vital, and intimate a situation that I could not imagine sharing it with just anyone. And if I could stand an occasional cup of coffee, I could not tolerate him as a regular visitor for meals. I was not thinking of the expense (he would no doubt bring something with him) or the waste of time. I only felt that I simply could not stand his presence at the head of the table (he would of course take the master's place) or the movement of his cheek muscles as he tried to eat with his mouth closed, and quite certainly not the way in which he would try to handle his knife and fork in my honor. Or if I was put at the head of the table and they took turns passing me the dishes that were farther away . . . I felt so bad that I could not even continue to develop my fantasy.

Tamara showed her willingness to serve by pouring me a second cup of coffee, and I thought that I would not be able to stand that either. When Kustaa Mauri was here she would of course look after my welfare in every possible way and make me feel one hundred per cent an invalid.

Tamara seemed to divine my thoughts—our intuitions do indeed reach out to each other in an unending caress—for she said:

"The matter can of course be arranged in such a way that you two do not meet at all, if you prefer. This is a big house. You can then reconsider the matter later. It's not impossible that your sexual potentialities might increase and extend too. Who knows, it might do you good to see us together. He wouldn't necessarily have to know about it. On the other hand, it may be good for him too. There are all kinds of possibilities, like those you get from reading second-rate sexy novels, though I suggest we reject those right from the start."

For some reason my imagination, always so reliable, failed

me at this point, just when I sorely needed it, and did not consent to give me any kind of foretaste of the situations that Tamara suggested. It was as if my imagination were actually locked up in a cupboard while the others were flirting outside. And I pictured how it would be forgotten there, until one day when the cupboard was opened by accident it would fall out, a withered skeleton, into someone's arms. And people would say: "Whose imagination was this, for heaven's sake?"

It was probably this horrid vision that caused me to say:

"Let's try it out in practice. How can one tell otherwise? Who knows how productive all this may prove."

Tamara received this communication quietly, without flinging her arms around my neck, and began to peel apples just as if she had known all along that we would reach this conclusion.

We continued for a long time to discuss the more precise details, as they came to Tamara's mind. We agreed that we would approach the matter gradually, a little at a time, and would see how the beginning turned out. Kustaa Mauri and I would not meet, at first at any rate; we would be spared introductions, how-do-you-dos, and formal conversation, which Tamara and I detest. Moreover, we wouldn't need to judge each other's physical person; we would avoid the possibility that Kustaa Mauri's appearance might immediately be so repugnant to me that a good idea would collapse in its infancy; the advantages of this decision were manifold.

"Don't worry," Tamara said, "remember that if you meet by accident he is the one who'll be surprised."

I could well believe that.

Kustaa Mauri was to arrive on one of those hot late-summer days that are made for love and the encounter of sweating bodies.

Tamara took a long time getting dressed; an achievement when one considers that she was wearing less clothes than ever. She pondered such matters as whether to put on a brassiere or not, and I don't know what she finally decided.

Then Tamara suddenly began to be concerned about her summer unsightliness, which she had zealously defended only a while before. And I must admit that I began to wonder whether this was really the same person as in winter, or whether human beings could change according to environment and season, even in character, as animals do. She did not make up, she used the sauna window as a mirror and—as she told me—the well when she was getting water, so that I would ask her, in *Kalevala* style, when she dawdled at the well: "Did'st thou once again thyself admire, thy picture long beholding?" She combed her hair straight back and tied it with a ribbon, and it cannot be claimed that this coiffure suited her, however natural and pure in style it might be. It made her face look larger and fatter and her cranium smaller, not in my opinion a favorable or attractive ratio, but one never knows of course what may attract anyone. The downy hair around the angles of her jaw, bleached by the sun, clearly showed, especially when she sat with the light behind her. Moreover, it could be distinguished more and more clearly the browner she became. The same was true of the mustache on her upper lip. On both sides of her nose and on her cheeks were freckles, as also on her arms. The outline of her lips was indistinct without lipstick, which she didn't use in summer. Something of the sweetness that glimmered in her face in winter was now distinctly lost, and she was more bare, older, and a trifle hard-looking. I tried to look at her as objectively as possible with the eyes of an outsider, and I have to admit that the sight as a whole was not particularly attractive; the fact that a person covers himself by various means obviously has other reasons than keeping warm, at least in our civilization. I seem to remember I recommended at this point that she should wear a brassiere, because then there would be at least a little more to take off; a little blouse and shorts are like an air flight on which one doesn't have time to relax or have a meal but only to lose one's soul, as the Japanese believe.

"You talk like an old aunt," she said, though listening with very evident interest.

"The aunt figure is ignored far too much in our society. It would have much to give busy people in this changing world."

"I have broken veins in my legs," said Tamara.

"Well, surely he has seen those before."

"Yes, but in a situation where I was in control. I wouldn't like him to start thinking about them while he was sitting on the shore."

"Put long pants on then."

"But that would look as if I was hiding things, on a hot

119

day like this. And anyway I'd have to uncover them. Better for him to see everything all at once when he comes. If I'm too repulsive to him then he'll surely invent some excuse and go away."

So it's like that, I thought. We are so much on our toes, so much prepared for the worst. It is for this kind of mental state that industry has developed waterproof and kissproof cosmetics; there is nothing that listens to our psyche so carefully as commercialism—and we ungrateful people criticize it.

"If only I had remembered to tell him on the phone that I'm ugly here—why didn't I remember to tell him that?" Tamara lamented. "He'll drive here and picture in his mind all the time a red-lipped creature with fluffy curls and then he'll meet a rough monocolored one, like a tree trunk, like a gray bat you can't tell from pine bark, a quite different person, with sleep dust in the corners of her eyes. What on earth shall I do? What if I just come out of the water, and meet him all dripping wet? That would give him time to get used to me. That's how it is. I'm no longer beautiful without beautification. Perhaps I ought to have gone to the hairdresser and said: 'Do this same thing artistically.' "

This seemed so promising that I began to get really enthusiastic. It was indeed interesting to see—or to hear— how Kustaa Mauri would react to this unembellished summer-Tamara who was like bare flesh; like a beefsteak, special offer, take it or leave it.

There were many dangers. Who knows, this reduced, basic woman might awaken his sense of honor, recalling chastity and the traditional Western virtues, under whose veil one can do whatever one likes, for instance deceiving another's hopes most cruelly. Who knows, he might suddenly want just to keep bees and train Doberman pinschers.

It seemed to me that ideas like these were floating in Tamara's mind too, for she suddenly stopped in the middle of varnishing her toenails and looked out of the window thoughtfully, in her hand the little brush with a drop of varnish the color of a tea rose on the end of it, her foot on the old chest. She did not say anything, but seemed for a moment unnecessarily serious.

"What is the sense in varnishing your toenails?" I said.

"Otherwise he won't see them in the grass," she answered.

I saw her from the side and suddenly she appeared before my eyes like a real live Doberman pinscher, smooth, alert, prepared for anything, unyielding. I wondered what spell I could cast so that Kustaa Mauri—my unknown friend—would see this similarity too. Or perhaps this was a message, sent from far away from him to me.

Before Kustaa Mauri's arrival, tempers had smoothed down all around, and a solemn, fateful "Take me as I am" spirit prevailed.

I withdrew in good time to my room at the other end of the house. I was well prepared with reading matter and had seen to the airing of the room. The window was provided with green fly netting, and behind that, in its own quickly woven netting, there was a large pale spider, whose movements I watched. Mostly it kept still, giving no sign of life, but as soon as one of the thousands of little syrphids, the flower flies cruising outside the window, grazed its web, it mounted a lightning attack in that direction, failing however to catch any of them. The screams of the young woodpeckers were muffled on this side of the house, but could be heard nonetheless, like a constant time signal. As they grew they had learned to some extent to be quiet and sleep. I had woken several times at night to find the world around dead silent. Or at least that is how it seemed at first, after hearing day in and day out that constant unbroken squawking.

Actually I spent quite a happy day, and thought a lot; I had not had my lone days here as normally, and it seemed that thoughts had piled up; it was a long time since I had enjoyed my aloneness. I composed in my mind an article on the subject of the "identity of the intelligentsia" which had been bothering me for some time, in fact from back in the spring. The final impetus for it had been given by my regular knife grinder, who on his last visit to me in spring said, as he rubbed my kitchen knives on his file at the table: "There is more mental stress nowadays than economic." He was a former painter and former alcoholic, one of those rare ones who had managed to overcome his habit. He lived on his national pension and his disability pension, moved around from place to place, painted pictures, ground knives when there were knives to grind, lived in lodging houses for men, read books, and kept himself clean. His idea was that the intelligentsia took unto itself the achievements of the working class by declaring that we are all workers. He considered this dishonest and said that everyone must be aware of his class status and admit it without shame. Education creates classes, as does industry, so why try to find excuses. You should write about it, since you have the right contacts, he said. Even the title of "worker" should not be used by just anyone who feels like it. We are exploited enough in the name of God without that.

I made some kind of outline for the article; it fascinated me more and more; I certainly would not get any peace before I had written it. It seemed a long time since everything had been as it should be, Tamara happy, I at work. I had no desire for anything more as I sat in the cool of my room and stared thoughtfully at the silhouette of the forest for so long that when I looked up toward the sky I saw everything white that I had just seen dark. I remembered how I amused myself as a child with afterimages and conjured trees full of dark suns.

I hardly heard anything, except for the sound of a car and the opening of doors, and I did not try to see anything. It may be that I am an exhibitionist, an erotomaniac and verbal fetishist, but a peeping Tom I am not. That became quite clear.

As the evening passed I saw how the spider succeeded in catching a fly. I noticed it from the fly's tremendous buzzing and thought it was coupling. But the fly was caught in the grasp of the web, and it took a long time before it began to lose consciousness and finally died. Many times after I thought it had fallen into a stupor, it still made a rattling noise with its wings and tried to wriggle free.

During the evening there also appeared at the window those hawk-shaped and heart-shaped little moths which are always connected in my mind with country life and summer nights, and which for some reason like to sit motionless on the window while many others fly back and forth restless and hurrying, as if they know the briefness of these light nights and of life. These last-mentioned moths appear toward the end of June; they are quite large and, as I said, restless, and I do not care for them especially. Not until much later do the little pale-gray evening moths appear, like a cloud or a tumble of feathers wherever one steps, bringing to the summer evening a sense of weddings and death. After the swallows, I await their coming most.

It was long since I had been filled with such a feeling of unselfishness. I was prepared to live to the end of my years in this room, even in a cupboard, as long as all was well with Tamara. I would have been ready to swear oaths, bribe providence, surrender whatever I still had to surrender. The idea of ransom and redemption is remarkably deep in man. I was moved by my own unselfishness, and for a short while I was completely convinced that in love, at least momentarily, the best in humanity is realized. I wanted to fight to hold on to this feeling. It would make me capable of anything.

They had had a wonderful day.

She slipped in beside me at four in the morning, with the sun shining directly on the bed. It had come up two hours before and they had watched it rise together. The lake had steamed, the rocks sweated, the woodpeckers screamed. Baby thrushes, unable to fly, had been on the path; they had learned to fly before their eyes. A dragonfly had mistaken Tamara for a water lily. And the flowers! Twinflowers, butterfly orchis, cranberry, tormentil covered the sides of the swamp basin like a bridal veil. They had even gone walking; they were both fond of swamps, swamps should be preserved. Nor was that all: they had managed to see water lizards, had eaten half-ripe strawberries and Kustaa Mauri's mouth had tasted of wood tick. And when they had come to the meadow all the high grass had been full of round spiders' webs, heavy with dew, like forgotten kites entangled with the grass tips, or targets left over from some nocturnal shooting match, with dandelion puffs and the death struggle of a moth for a bull's eye; seines of dreams, their catch a gleam; whoever has seen them in the red light of dawn will never again wish to destroy them.

She was slippery and throbbing.

And holding me against her, she said: "Good God, how I love, how I can love, how good I am at loving."

And Kustaa Mauri had said that he had not believed that love existed, that it was like this, that he had reached a plateau, the midsummer of his life. He had not known that there was so much joy, that it was so great a joy.

And Kustaa Mauri had said: "Do I reach deep enough in you?" And Tamara had answered, though it was not quite true: "Of course you do." And Kustaa Mauri hardly knew what to do; how could he have remained so inexperienced? But at any rate it had been the first time, and Tamara had overflowed like a fountain. They had trembled with joy against one another, hardly able to believe that it was true.

"Just what happened?" I asked.

"Oh, if I only knew," Tamara said.

But she tried to remember.

"After all, I had chosen him with my heart, from everyone. Then I thought I wouldn't frighten him anymore by being so active. I even managed to forget why we were together—me, just imagine! Yet my decision was made, irrevocable."

"Frankly, I can't make head or tail of that," I remarked.

"I enjoyed his presence. Every inch of my skin seemed to be a sex organ, like a tapeworm's. And near him I feel big and strong. But I couldn't help being nervous and so was he; he told me that I was wrong not to participate with my whole personality. It seems I become deadly serious though I have such a strong sense of humor. It was the first time anyone wanted me to be comic in bed. I was very moved when he valiantly explained that it all depended on me; he wouldn't take any responsibility at all—that's his way of getting out of an embarrassing situation. All in all, I decided that to mix sex and comedy wasn't so stupid and while I was thinking of that I started absentmindedly to play with him. What funny little things penises are, I thought, almost like domestic animals. Some are lively, some flop all over the place, some like to be petted, others can't stand to be touched. I remember I scratched it, like a dog under the chin. And when I began to feel it getting bigger I thought I was imagining it. But it went on growing until you couldn't mistake it, as if air had got into a balloon at last after you'd hopelessly puffed into it for hours. I felt giddy. The next moment I was afraid it would flop down again any minute, as often happens, and tried not to pay too much attention to it; above all I tried not to be afraid because fear is catching. So I rubbed it again a little, casually, as if the whole thing was quite unimportant, and kept chatting—sorry, I really don't remember what, something amusing it was anyway, because he chuckled quietly. And it seemed as if it was ready at last and he got on top of me to put it in and my God how I was afraid it wouldn't come off and we'd never manage it and he was afraid too because he started thrashing around and poked me with it without finding the right place and when he finally managed to push it in it was like an awl. Like a willow whistle. Some men tickle and pinch women, I can't imagine why—I suppose they think it feels good. I suspect some sex guide is guilty of spreading such ideas. I've met two men before that did it— Kustaa Mauri was the third. I thought, let him get on with it, the main thing is to sever the maidenhood of our relationship, I can cure him of the habit later. It didn't take very long, and he couldn't get practically anything out of the orgasm, he just spilled it out inside me and suddenly it felt as if there was an angleworm inside me."

"And that was all?"

"Yes. It was the first time. I hope you got some idea of how blissful it was. I felt that nothing so tremendous had happened to me before. That's how it feels whenever it's successful."

"I am sorry, but my experience in reliving all this was incomplete," I said. "Perhaps I was also too tense. I didn't reach the climax."

"Oh, nor did I of course," Tamara said. "But you can't ask for everything at once. I did say this was only the first time. You haven't the least idea what the second was like."

"No, I haven't. I am burning with desire to hear about it."

She lay for some time with her eyes closed, naked, resting. The telling had exhausted her. Her face had the relaxed expression of a woman who'd been loved, the wrinkles smoothed away by kisses.

Looking at this body that I loved and of which I could never partake, even to the limited extent to which man and woman succeed in reaching each other, I again had the feeling, special yet familiar, that I was neither man nor woman. I was a stump, all that remains when branches and trunk are cut, the only sign of life wild shoots, like incurable dreams.

After some time Tamara said: "Do you want to hear about the second time now or later?"

"This seems to be the right time."

"I got on top of him, like this, and put him quietly into me. I explained to him that this stage mustn't be rushed, it's one of the best."

"Was he . . . ?"

"I made him ready, I kneaded him like dough, I said, 'Pat-a-cake, pat-a-cake, baker's man,' and got him standing that way. If only you knew how wonderful that feels for a woman. I never want to lose that creative joy. I felt as if I were building a human being, making myself a sweetheart, a gingerbread boy that came alive, grew up a bit at a time. That organ really has the flexibility and hardness needed in life. The capacity to change is rare, and the penis is its living symbol. Then I started to move so it was nice for me, without hurrying, rocking like this. It's funny, I can't stand slowness, but in lovemaking I like a slow pace, making it last as long as possible. I realized that I was teaching this to a man for the first time, and wondered whether I'd regret it one day. He said: 'You're good at this natural dance.' "

"Tell me how it feels for a woman."

"On top or underneath?"

"Whichever you like. Just tell."

"I prefer to be on top. Then you can get the movement and the feeling to correspond to each other. You feel freer," Tamara began emphatically. Then a sudden gust of shyness came over her: "I can't describe it."

I caught hold of her arms, pressed with all my strength, then let my fingers wander until she moaned.

"Tell me, Tamara. Does it feel like eating and drinking?"

"In feels better than out."

"But that's obvious."

"Not to him."

"Unbelievable!"

"Yes. What a discovery!"

At that moment we took fire, and my mind was showered with never-before-experienced ideas and images, as if my temperature had suddenly risen. That's how I'll die, from the presence of my imaginings, Tamara's weight on my body, her lips, teeth, and tongue on my neck, her arm underneath me.

Tamara began to laugh as a tired and happy person laughs without knowing why, and shook against my stomach.

"You're crushing my pubis."

"That's what he said too."

But now identifying no longer stimulated me, nor did I

have any desire to ride on Kustaa Mauri's verbal wings; they would scarcely have borne me anyway. I wanted to say something original.

"I love you. Did he say he loved you too?"

"Well, not just like that. People don't say things like that because it's supposed to be a cliché. He did speak about classical love, how wonderful and unbelievable it is. And then he said I am strongly present wherever he goes. What would he mean by that?"

"Perhaps that he does not need to meet you often."

"Perhaps," said Tamara humbly.

But an instant later she was sitting up with clenched fists.

"I have created this man. I have molded him with my own hands. I have a right to him. The right of these hands."

How easy it would have been to say something light, like "Hurry up and have a written contract drawn up." But people must have their dramatic moments. And that is why we are together, Tamara and I; so as not to need to shake our fists at empty walls. "It's important for love to be realized," I said aloud. "It's not enough to get love in return, a world must be created where the he-and-I combination can come true."

Tamara opposed this idea vehemently.

"No. Love must be secret. In the modern world that is absolutely necessary. In telling one gives it away, exposes it to others who simply tear it apart. But to one another we must express every feeling; in this way love gradually increases in the world."

"Was the second time the best then?" I asked.

Tamara thought for a while.

"I can't really say. The third, fourth, and fifth times are usually the best. After that you have to find variations, in one way or another, read something, or play tricks, be a bit capricious."

I began to get sleepy, but events that were just becoming memories now flooded constantly into Tamara's mind.

"He said our love is like Baroque music. What could he

have meant by that?" she said, and after thinking it over for a minute herself replied:

"Perhaps he meant it comes first, and afterward all the other music. Or did it mean it's unbelievable?"

"I think Baroque music is filling. Shall we eat something? I feel weak." (Nothing is as exhausting as a mental orgasm.)

Tamara lay down on the bed and stretched her hands above her head as was her habit.

"When I'm in love I can love everyone, the whole world. There's enough in me now for heavens knows how many, like extra breast milk."

Tempted by the overproduction of milk, I asked: "So you love me too?"

"I love you like a devastated landscape. Do you know, we saw spruce trees with only one branch left alive, growing twisted with head down on a slope. They reminded me of you."

And soon afterward: "Imagine, he accepted me like this, ugly. I appealed to him just like this. He said that to him I was like a Doberman pinscher, his pinschers, and that he suddenly knew how I should be handled."

"It's he who handled you, is it?" I mumbled, exhausted by cerebral eroticism. I started to get out of bed to fetch myself a sandwich.

"Well, if he wants to imagine that, he can. He too has his illusions."

"Yes, of course," I said, on my way to the refrigerator.

"What an extremely interesting process," I heard Tamara saying from the bed. "A small, limp organ hardens, lengthens, and rises upright to a position of attack. It must be as significant a phenomenon for the man as the whole biological cycle is for the woman. At that moment he invests his whole blood circulation. An ejaculation isn't sufficiently appreciated. It corresponds to woman's whole cycle of secretions, the hormonal changes that give rhythm to a woman's adulthood. Ejaculation must have an immense spiritual significance,

130

whether the man admits it or not. And to the woman too, whether she admits it or not. I admit it. One can't demand more from a man. He's enormously exposed in the sexual act, even if the woman is unaware of it. Though on the other hand it's something that is outside the man and only attached to him. Woman has to open herself every time."

"True," I shouted with my mouth full.

I found some cucumber and cold veal in the refrigerator, and started to make sandwiches for us.

The evening of the same day we realized suddenly that it was quiet. In the heat many of the birds did not sing, and grasshopper time had not yet come. From the woodpecker nest not the slightest sound could be heard. We thought at once of a violent end, for it seemed difficult to believe that the departure of the young from the nest could have occurred without our noticing. But that was apparently what had happened. We waded through the jungle of wild chervil, already over, to the nest, examined it and sniffed at it, even measured its depth with a stick. There were no signs of struggle or death in the neighborhood, nor any message to say that all was well either.

Tamara and Kustaa Mauri wanted at this stage to meet every day; maybe it was a mistake, I don't know.

They went on trips in the surrounding countryside. Kustaa Mauri arrived at odd times of the day or night, whenever he found a suitable moment. Something unbelievable was happening to him, and to protect it he had to create a believable atmosphere.

I never saw him come, seldom even heard any sound, except once when he arrived in a small seaplane straight from the heavens just when Tamara had started to think that a day had come when he would not appear. The plane circled over the yard several times before landing, and aroused in us that primitive surge of emotions that a low-flying plane always does. Tamara ran out onto the veranda, I hobbled to the window. The plane lost height and landed before our eyes, raising a flash of water into the air on both sides. Then it turned and swam leisurely to the shore between water-lily leaves that quivered in the airstream, like a tame swan, unbelievable and unreal, and when I left the window I knew that from its inside Kustaa Mauri stepped straight into the embrace of Tamara, who had run to the jetty.

Tamara was swollen with love and with the heat; it was difficult for her to sit. I bathed, anointed, and cooled the sore spot. She said that it distinctly relieved the burning and hastened recovery; for some reason every now and then she felt that time was short and had to be used carefully.

Nevertheless she kept repeating: "I won't give him up. I have a right to him. Without me he wouldn't have this side of life at all, he's said so himself. I'm not taking anything from anyone."

I tried sometimes to analyze the possibility of his leaving her; it did not appear very likely. Tamara told me that Kustaa Mauri kept repeating "unbelievable, this is unbelievable," and for some reason this gave me great satisfaction. I would like to believe in the unbelievable, to marvel at marvels. At moments like this I felt I loved Kustaa Mauri, or rather the joy he must feel.

"Imagine," said Tamara, "he's lived all his life thinking he's not worth anything, and performed so poorly that it wasn't worth bothering about. I've liberated him from that. A new world has opened up for him, another life."

"How does marriage fit into this pattern?" I said. I could not help asking this question, even though I knew how much she disliked all allusions to marriage, no matter how objective.

She reared now like a horse plagued by a fly: "There are all kinds of marriages. Anyway, stop talking about it. It's a fruitless subject of conversation."

"So when you say you will not give Kustaa Mauri up you do not mean marriage?"

Tamara at times can look at me in a way that makes me feel ten times more crippled than I am; this time she looked as if I were a Cyclops stewing its brains for supper.

"How can you go on about something that I explained years ago. I'm not interested in people's marriages. I simply don't wish to know about them. I never ask anything. I listen if I'm forced to. And I never, absolutely never, would steal another woman's husband. The very idea makes me want to vomit. You really know me very little, I must say."

I thought that the same nausea would cover several more questions, so I continued boldly:

"But supposing some wife—let's not talk about Kustaa Mauri now, or why not talk about him"—I became bolder with my own boldness—"gets to know that you are having something to do with her husband . . ."

"She won't. I said before that love must be absolutely secret."

"But supposing," I insisted, "the man has pangs of conscience and tells his wife all."

Tamara's eyes widened. Evidently she had never considered such a possibility.

"Tell his wife! I don't have anything to do with imbeciles like that. No, that's impossible."

"What if he became religious?"

"With me? I could understand if someone might thank God afterward. I've done that many times."

"Or talk in his sleep. Start sighing 'Tamara, Tamara.'"

She became thoughtful. Then she said:

"I do know there are men who want to hurt their wives with confessions. I know them by instinct. They talk about honesty as an excuse to give her the pains of hell, to see her suffer. It makes them feel powerful, compensates for their own lack of self-assurance. I avoid that kind like the plague."

"Well then," I said triumphantly, "so you admit the truth would hurt."

"Of course. It always hurts. There's a woman hiding in every wife. That's why one shouldn't tell. Truth nearly always hurts, and in this case is unnecessary."

"But is that morally right?" I said, although I agreed with her. We had not talked like this for a long time, and I had

134

missed discussing these same old questions; repetition nourishes domesticity.

"It's highly moral," Tamara said, obviously enjoying her favorite expression. "Or it's on a higher level of morality, where essential and individual values are important. This has nothing to do with conventional honesty. Generally I explain this clearly to the man I'm with, if there's the slightest sign that his ideas are on the wrong wavelength. And if he is still doubtful, I consider him a hopeless case. I announce right away that I'm on the wife's side and that he must be good to his wife, especially if he's happy with me. Quite a few then confess that they agree. Naturally there are the characters who say they're not understood and have been sleeping in the hall for the past six months. I don't bother with that kind."

"So you reject a whole unhappy group of people."

"Maybe, but I'm not perfect. An honest neurotic I do like, though I'm trying to change now with a commonplace man. Kustaa Mauri is wonderfully boring sometimes. He's like a wingless bird. You can't even imagine a man like that."

"Why not?"

"Because your soul flies. Because our souls fly together. He can never follow the flight of my soul, but it doesn't matter. I'm glad to return to him on earth. And sometimes I'd like to stay down. It's heavy work taking off and landing."

"Don't you rest with him? Love is rest, the only rest a human being has. And nothing is so exhausting. It is freedom, yet nothing binds so much. That is the paradox of love. Without love one is the prisoner of loneliness, even though one is so free alone. I rest in your nearness, although when you go away I am very tired. 'Be my rest.' It is an ethical imperative."

"Up to now I've found rest only with neurotics, those that bring the most sorrow; disturbed people seek each other out, the stressed sleep in each other's arms, sufferings couple and beget new ones, but always somewhere in between they find rest in each other, as if parallel lines against all laws crossed in secret before they continued their journey into infinity."

I always enjoyed it when she spoke like this, exciting herself into using high-flying words. I knew she was not in the habit of doing this in anyone else's company. In this sense I meant freedom for her.

While we were talking a thunderstorm had come up on the other side of the lake, behind the wooded ridges, where such storms are always said to come up in these parts. We hoped that the rain would freshen the air, but the humidity only increased and made the air still heavier to breathe. Perspiration trickled down our spines, and our conversation languished. In the midst of a thunderstorm a man feels very small, but he feels intensely that he exists. I mentioned this phenomenon to Tamara as the thunderclaps sounded a little less close and the torrent rattling on the windows became a steady domestic rain.

"Perhaps it's because man is always instinctively a bit afraid," she said, "and has at that moment a very concrete point of comparison for himself."

"So the clarity of the point of comparison is also important."

"Of course. And that's something man seldom has in practice. Only his fantasies are absolute. And that's the trouble."

"In practice or in fantasies?"

"Neither—in absoluteness."

"But surely in fantasies it is permitted?"

"Well, yes. But man controls his thoughts too, he's afraid to be free even in his innermost self, he feels guilty about his concepts and fantasies. Actually that shows how real his experience of them is. One should tell people: 'Your fantasies are yours alone, be free and bold in them.' "

"But fantasies are even confined by knowledge," I argued. "My sexual fantasies for instance are tied to mythology. I'd like to experience with you all the different ways in which the

136

gods have united with human beings, the golden rain included. That is not freedom. Then there are the insects' ways, which are even more imaginative than the practices of the gods. Invertebrates really have erotic imagination, and the lower on the scale one goes, the more fantastic the forms. If we were a pair of *bonellia viridis*, I would live as a parasite between your legs"—"Monotonous," Tamara said—"and would wish for nothing more from my life. What a bath, what ecstasy! I have not studied them very carefully, but as far as I can see birth only means that the male moves from the female's stomach to her sexual organs. The localizing of sensation in the higher animals is a definite retrogression."

"When you fall in love that ability partly returns."

"What ability?"

"The ability to sense with one's whole body. Think of the effect of a touch of the knees, or the way in which an elbow becomes a sexual organ the moment the loved one clasps it with his hand. Even my hair wriggles when Kustaa Mauri takes my head between his hands, and every square inch of me is like a suction cup. Yet at the same time I am open and free, so free that I soar."

As the rain continued I thought I noticed in Tamara a new type of restlessness. I knew quite well that she could not stand being shut up in this house with me for many days. Besides, I didn't expect anything like that of her. I would have been irritated by her restlessness, however effectively concealed. The existence of our relation depended to a large degree on admitting this fact—that we would never live together permanently. Every holiday reminded us of the validity of this concept. I saw her look first toward the road, then toward the lakeside windows; perhaps she imagined Kustaa Mauri would, through rain and storm, appear from the mists like the Swan of Finland or the Flying Dutchman. It was the first evening this summer when light was necessary, but she could not even bear to hear electricity mentioned. So I dug out a large candle and lighted it, thankful that at least she let me use matches. The world outside the windows seemed darkened even by this little twinkle just as if autumn had understood that it was permissible to step into our lives after this summer and gradually settle into our evenings. I too kept an eye on the windows now, and after a while there occurred what happens everywhere on the first dark evenings of July where there is long grass around the house—many different kinds of moths of varying sizes gather on the windows, some of them glue themselves in place for some reason, some ripple ceaselessly against the glass like virtuoso skaters, while the big hawk moths, which are plentiful in these parts, drum with their whole bodies against the window as if someone were constantly tapping with his forefinger, trying to get in. I don't know to what extent Tamara noticed this, but her restlessness grew constantly. She shifted from one room to another, complained about scattered clothing drooping here and there (most of which was her own), claimed she could smell a funny odor, and began to make up a tale about skeletons buried under the foundations of the house (skeletons do not normally smell any longer, I ventured to point out), after which she started to consider which of us three would be murdered if two reached unanimity and who the unanimous two might be. It began to seem to me too that the odor of the old clothes in the cupboards and of the people who had worn them spread around the house because of the humidity and affected our thoughts through our breathing. I lighted another candle because I thought they would dry the air and burn the odors away; we had not managed to get a fire going in the open fireplace and thought that there may be a bird's nest in the chimney, so we did not try again. I struck matches one after another, until Tamara observed that the smell of sulphur suited my nature well.

It began to appear evident that rain and just the two of us in an empty house did not suit our lives at this stage. I say empty because it was obvious that we were not now able to people it for each other. I decided to take this quietly, since this was not the first time, but I did permit melancholy to flow freely through my mind. Actually it was very suitable on such a rainy evening. I came to think about walking; how Tamara had described her walk with Kustaa Mauri through the swamps and woods, where only the broken, dying spruces that hung on the slopes were a reminder of me. Suddenly I felt a piercing bitterness and jealousy. I could see Kustaa Mauri climbing the slope and stretching out a hand to Tamara to help her up; I saw their legs moving at the same pace on the rocks where there was room for them to walk abreast; I saw Kustaa Mauri jumping over a fallen tree trunk and kicking a big pine cone on the path. And I saw them going bathing, Kustaa Mauri conquering the bog pool by swimming across it and bringing back late wild rosemary between his teeth for Tamara. I tried to calm myself by thinking how good it is to make acquaintance with the sensation of jealousy; a person who has not felt it does not know anything of life. It is a piercingly pure and clear feeling, it strikes one's consciousness without warning, it burns like ice, strips whatever it touches. It is a genuine and powerful experience, just what I desire to enhance and supplement my life, to move my mind. But for some reason I did not succeed in convincing myself of the value of this experience, it remained in the extremities of my soul like glue on the fingers; I did not manage to detach it and mold it aesthetically and ethically into a satisfactory entity that I could control, like a little statue that I might place with the others in my constantly growing collection. So that I decided to reject it and not think about it anymore. This rejection was justified, I thought. I even invented a name for it: conscious rejection.

So the day went by. The rain had decided to quell the heat, and in the end it succeeded. When the wind had calmed down we opened the windows and fresh cool air flooded in for the first time in weeks. For a while it seemed that we had been waiting only for this, and that the coming of the coolness was quite sufficient purpose for this day. I revelled in advance at the thought of a refreshing, unperspiring night with the rain rattling on the roof and the hawk moths tapping on the windows, a benevolent dusk over the landscape.

Evidently Tamara's thoughts did not tune in with mine at all, for it seemed to me she was already running to the steps before the car's lamps lanced the darkness and illuminated the room twice as brightly as the lightning, striking first one, then another window. I saw her standing on the steps in the rain, her arms outstretched as the car lights shone straight on her and came nearer and nearer. Then she started to run to the car and I turned to wander off into my room.

Thus the day achieved a happy ending: Kustaa Mauri had come after all.

I began to suspect that in spite of his glorified everydayness he commanded the art of keeping a person waiting, the technique of absence, extremely well, was a real master in its use, to the point of binding even Tamara, that expert in disappointment. I thought I would warn her, then decided it was useless. When have warnings helped in these matters? Besides, she had herself said: "I can't stand waiting," and had proved it today.

My room had cooled down sharply during the rain, and when I got there I wondered for a moment what was bothering me. Then I realized: I was simply cold. I had forgotten what it felt like. Interesting: a kind of tension, one of many.

It rained all night. I intended to stay awake to hear when Kustaa Mauri left, but then I thought, what would I do with that knowledge?

At some point Tamara slid in beside me. She came into the room where I slept and crowded into the narrow bed that was too small even for me.

"I feel I exist only in an orgasm, but it doesn't give me a feeling of continuity," she said, and I thought I heard a faint note of despair in her voice, or was I only dreaming? "I long for continuity, for the feeling of wholeness. I've decided to seek it—I don't need much of it, I'd be satisfied with very little, the minimum."

I made room for her by my side, drew her close to me, thinking, I am her father and she is my little girl. I stroked her hair; children and animals like having their heads patted; perhaps Kustaa Mauri patted her thinking of his Doberman pinschers. Once again I experienced the feeling that I would give all that was left of me for her to reach harmony, so that continuity would once again be born in her, that blessed state, though so little valued nowadays.

And I knew too what her minimum meant. It meant the same as mine: only to feel one's existence.

And before I fell asleep again, I rubbed out in my mind the word "only."

During the weeks that our holiday lasted, Tamara found time to get acquainted with the farmers from the neighboring house. She had already met them several times earlier when she had come to look at the place. In addition they had the best possible subject of conversation to facilitate getting to know each other: the quarrelsome heirs about whom everyone knew sufficiently little but enough dramatic facts to be able to censure them without pangs of conscience. The most vehement and loud-voiced of them was, it appeared, the dentist, for he was accustomed to speaking without being answered back, having stuffed his listener's mouth full of instruments. One of the heirs was a lawyer and his presence in particular threatened to make for unending strife, since he was able to refute the others' opinions with legal clauses so that agreement, which now and then seemed possible, always vanished far beyond the horizon after he had spoken. Besides, he regularly got his fee as executor of the estate, as the bundle of papers in his briefcase grew. Only one person, an alcoholic artist whose address was not known to anyone, had agreed to take his part of the inheritance in money and kept out of the quarrel. He had been given thirty thousand marks and had never even asked what percentage of the total estate it was, unable to doubt the fairness of the other heirs. This had apparently been the only thing about which the heirs were unanimous. They had all felt relief at getting rid of this highly dubious person, who according to rumor had long ago left his family, though he went to see them, and even spoke of his children without showing the slightest sign of shame.

The farm had precise information on all these points, because the family meetings, which were often held on the spot, as for instance the division of the movable property that had lasted many days, required from time to time an outsider and all kinds of witnesses of signatures, and each one had come with his own papers and explained the matter from his own point of view. Besides, they had needed milk and eggs and potatoes; they had fetched water from the well because the well of the villa had a rusty taste from disuse. Someone had wanted sour milk for his hangover, someone had wanted to buy farm butter unaware that such an article existed no longer, had admired the home-baked bread and departed happily with a warm loaf under his arm. "If they had known, if they had known," the farmer's wife had sighed from time to time as she told Tamara about the original owners. They were such quiet, unassuming people, and very thrifty, respectable in every way; who could have dreamed they were so wealthy and had such terrible relations. They liked smoked spareribs that cost only three marks a kilo at the shop. Lovely people, a pity they weren't still alive.

The farmer's wife had asked Tamara about me. He is my uncle and I myself am engaged, Tamara had replied.

"Why such an explanation?" I asked.

"I wanted to spare her worry. I saw how it relieved her at once. She had already invented who knows what tale about us in her imagination, and it was making it a lot more difficult for us to get on together. She started to make coffee straightaway, and good coffee she made too. And gave me homemade doughnuts—I haven't had doughnuts like that since I was a child. She asked whether you wouldn't like to come and visit them too, your life must be miserable and hard with legs like that, she said."

"I hope you refused politely enough on my behalf."

"Of course. I said you had adapted well and that the richness of your intellectual life compensated for the limitations of your physical life. She understood that completely. I noticed she had a thick book called *Fruits of the Spirit* on the shelf under the radio. Then I said that you do research work, study the psychology of language, and are interested in dialects. Then she asked what was wrong with your legs."

"What did you say to that?"

"I said your wife shot you in the back when you were trying to run away with another woman."

"Was that version really necessary?"

"Absolutely necessary. I thought it over for a second before I answered. Now she doesn't feel sorry for you anymore. If I had said you're a war invalid and full of shrapnel or the victim of a car accident, our conversation wouldn't have relaxed at all and I should have had to keep on inventing more things."

To tell the truth, when I thought over the matter more carefully I felt a certain relief also. It was as if I had suddenly become a respectable citizen in the eyes of those around me. Perhaps I might go and visit them sometime, or we might invite them here. It might be interesting to study the preservation of dialect more closely.

"I think I will send them a book the next time you go there. Perhaps *The Agricultural Crisis* when I have read it myself, and then I have that *Mysteries of the Middle East,* although I don't read crime novels myself; I don't know how it has got mixed up with my books," I jabbered on, carried

144

away with my desire for social intercourse. I was quite aware that I might actually send a book; it was my way of keeping up human relations. But there would be no social life for me, that relief I had given myself years ago with a free heart. I kept company only with those people I really wanted to meet and in whose opinions I was at least to some extent interested. Of them I have already mentioned my regular knife grinder and armless raker, both of whom I had met through Tamara. Then there were some people with whom I was in desultory correspondence, real friends to whom it was unnecessary ever to explain anything, and a few compulsory acquaintances who in spite of my efforts I did not manage to avoid. But in Tamara there are many people; sometimes for the sake of simplicity I would have liked to take away half her egos, even though she complains of suffering from depersonalization.

The spiritual mainstay of the farm was the old mistress, Tamara said; she had known the owners of the villa best and knew most about the heirs. Actually the farm was in the hands of the youngest son, the only one of a trio of brothers who had been interested in farming; the two others had moved to the city to study and live an urban life. The son had a wife, a fair, quiet woman with strong arms, who seemed to be well aware of the changing status of agriculture in Finnish society and augmented Tamara's knowledge with many new insights, so that I had to listen to exhaustion to the advantages of silo grass over dried hay and yawningly to deprecate the use of antibiotics in cattle fodder. Tamara had also talked with the farmer, tried to stop him using toxins to destroy the brush beside the roads and ditches. She had talked about poisons gathering at the end of the food chain and damage to the fetus. I asked—a yawn again confusing my words—whether she had really discussed serious matters with them; if so, I was prepared to listen in honor of her ability to interfere with other people's personal affairs.

"She started to talk to me herself. I seem to be the kind

of person that people start telling their sorrows to. In their case it's childlessness. She was washing the milk pans in the dairy and started to talk to me about it. In the barn there were two newborn calves and one of them had diarrhea and a big mother rabbit that had eleven young ones, she had had them by her own son. All the necessary associations were laid on, in fact."

In such charming circumstances began a brief episode that shocked us, linking us unexpectedly with the farm folk. Or linking Tamara with them and me through her, which is usual in our life.

The young mistress had spoken openly to Tamara; there is, in Tamara's way of listening, that particular objective interest that makes people open up. They had been married for seven years, and wanted a child all that time. Soon they would hardly dare speak to each other for fear that the painful subject would come up. Tamara had urged going to the doctor. There had in fact been some sort of visit to the doctor. There should be a thorough examination, said Tamara. And both should be examined. "You can't get them to, not men," the young woman said, blushing. Tamara had insisted, encouraged her, explained and coaxed as if she had her own stake in the matter. She knew many couples who had been married for seven or even nine years and had children after that. And think of all the things they could do nowadays: blow the tubes open, peep inside, straighten out wombs, make a whole bunch of ova grow instead of one so that women who had been considered barren all their lives gave birth to triplets and quadruplets in one go to the wonder and envy of all. But the husband must be examined too.

She had talked like an agricultural adviser, been given a cup of coffee in the kitchen like an artificial insemination expert, felt that she was doing good and was a world reformer. She admitted all this to me tearfully afterward, but by then the situation was such that I could no longer help.

146

The matter came up again whenever Tamara went to buy eggs and when the first new potatoes were groped for in the soil without pulling the stems, and many times when they met at the mailbox and stayed talking there. They had become friends in this way, called each other by their first names, and Tamara had repeated: "You should go to the doctor, both of you should be examined."

And so the day had come when the young wife had decked herself out in her city clothes and gone to the doctor's, got a certificate from her local doctor and queued up at the polyclinic, come back after the examination exhausted by the heat and the bus journey, with an appointment fixed for her husband in her handbag together with instructions for taking a sperm specimen. Reluctance, shyness, awkwardness were overcome, and in spite of practical difficulties a fresh specimen was obtained, a new day dawned, and the farmer's wife went off to the city again with hope in her heart.

She seems to have returned by the 6:30 bus, for I remember that the sun had already dropped behind the forest but was still shining on the pines that grew near the rocks, making their trunks glow. When she returned the house was empty, the old woman was milking, the husband was in the meadow beyond the lake with his tractor, so that the wife had had an opportunity to consider for a moment where to hide the diagnosis. She had taken the Bible from the shelf under the radio and put the paper inside it in case her husband when he came should want to see it and perhaps look for it arbitrarily in her handbag. Immediately afterward she had, however, felt that she did not have the strength to meet any member of the family just then, and she had taken the Bible under her arm and run off into the woods to cry there. Then she had seen in the distance her husband's tractor coming home, changed her direction, remembered Tamara, and decided to take refuge with her; tell her what had happened and perhaps hide with her that evening.

147

I heard her running up the high veranda steps and as soon as she saw Tamara let out a cry that reminded me from my childhood of the bellowing of a cow by the remnants of her slaughtered calf. The woman had had the Bible in her hands and she had pushed it toward Tamara unable to speak a word of explanation. For a moment Tamara thought she was out of her mind. "Then I understood that it was only sorrow, despair settling in her. She fought against it with her crying and that was healthy," Tamara said afterward.

I had gone at once to my room, so that I came to know about this moment of pain through Tamara, in accordance with the rules of my life.

They had looked for the report on the sperm specimen between the pages of the Bible; it had been suitably placed among the Lamentations of Jeremiah. The paper said briefly that in the whole ejaculation there had been only a few live sperm cells and even they moved with difficulty. The possibilities of fertilization were astronomically small, the doctor had said. Of course they could bring a new sample after some time, if they wished. But from the clinical point of view there was nothing to remark. There are other values in life, and childless couples often stay closer to one another.

The woman did not remember whether she had started to cry as soon as she heard this. She had sat paralyzed in the bus, concentrating all her strength on just hanging on till she reached her own stop, had tried to think of a way to tell the news as if it were nothing, without succeeding in finding one. She had thought of suggesting a trip to the Canaries with the Farmers' Club, or that they should sell some wood and enlarge the barn, or build a silo tower. But nothing had helped.

"It's not for myself," she kept repeating, "not myself, but Ilmari won't be able to stand it; all the time he's been afraid it's his fault, and I know he won't say anything, just go silent, bear it from day to day, as long as he lives, blame himself

148

that I am not married to someone who could give me children. . . . I would give everything," she started again, "everything that the fault was in me. I would be stronger to bear it."

I heard her crying from my room; it seemed to keep starting again before she managed to finish the previous outburst. I knew that Tamara would let her cry and would cry with her; women have this irreplaceable ability to help each other in this way. From the broken sentences that carried to my ear, I already understood everything, and in understanding I felt the enormous weight of guilt that had fallen on Tamara to bear, as if it were crushing my heart too.

"This is the end of life for us," I heard the woman say, "after this everything is just carrying on, the purpose is gone, hope is gone."

The anguish, helplessness, and guilt infected me too. It was a long time since I had felt my own life so hopeless. Indeed how had I managed to act this comedy? No, I hadn't even been an actor—a mere scene shifter, a scarecrow, a hole in the wall, threatening the whole structure.

The young woman had left in the end, her face swollen but calmed, her tears used up, having decided to tell her husband everything simply and frankly, holding his hand, wordlessly praying that he forgive her for the fault not being hers.

Tamara's turn for grief came only afterward.

"Who do I think I am, advising others, exhorting them?" she lamented. "They would have lived on in happy ignorance, hoping from one year to another, getting used to it little by little, understanding gradually, growing into the knowledge gently. Now they have to stand this suffering. Perhaps they'll become closed off from one another completely, perhaps they won't want to be together anymore at all. I often imagine becoming pregnant. It's a fascinating fantasy. I wouldn't like to lose it ever, not at any price. If only I knew how to pray,

I feel a need to pray for them. The first prayer must have been born out of this kind of agony. Maybe it even created the god who was prayed to.

"Please, O God, do not separate them from one another, do not let them become dead to each other, make those few sperm cells move, create more new and healthy ones. That wouldn't be much for you to manage."

"Amen," I said, quite seriously.

For a moment I searched in my mind for a name for our feelings, then I found it: piety, a rare emotion, at least for people like us. To what could I compare it? Candlelight in the coolness and quiet of a church on a hot day, amid the clamor of the city; the playing of the organ when a good but distant person has died; flowers that open in one's lap during the blessing of the dead.

"I'm doing wrong in forcing myself into people's lives," Tamara mourned. "After this how can I dare to do anything? And I've boasted that I create life, that everything I lay my hand on becomes alive, like Kustaa Mauri. How can I dare after this to write even a simple recommendation? Like that woman I sent to Majorca to rest, she was quite worn out and her fingers were bent with rheumatism, she fell in love with another man on that trip and all her life is upside down now, I haven't been able to tell even you about it, the children are heaven knows where, with relations and in children's homes, and the man is suing for divorce. Dear God forgive me. Tell me what is really wrong with us."

"Life is not fit for man," I said, still deeply serious.

"It is not. It is not."

Once again we had that rare moment of unanimity that every now and then lights up the existence of the human species. Tamara sat on the floor in front of the bow window, eyes shut and wiping her nose constantly with the long hanging bow of her blouse collar, which had been neatly tied during the day in Kustaa Mauri's honor.

I sat on a low stool before the fireplace and thought that

the simplest thing to do would be to put my head in the lap of my private psychophysiotherapist, console her by reminding her that after all I was here, a creature that lacked a considerable quantity of man's cursed qualities, she should not forget that. But what should happen—my crawling did not work this time, perhaps I did not concentrate on it sufficiently, perhaps due to my state of mind I did not send harsh enough commands to my knees, for they did not hold up at all now, only dropped me unaesthetically on the floor. Tamara could not help laughing.

"I'm sorry, but you look more like a caterpillar than a cripple. Actually one could believe that you're still at some early stage of evolution which might develop unexpected dimensions."

This was naturally a very welcome turn in our conversation, and to encourage it I lay down full length on the floor and rolled in a moment to Tamara. Without exaggerating I can say that this occurred at miraculous speed, and I remember my mother saying that I had never crawled like other children, but rolled from one place to another, and had done it very skillfully; I had a tender, loving mother who had watched all my ways with interest and made me feel with her caresses that I was a pleasant and valued creature; it is possible that I still have within me scraps of this store of love which still help me daily.

I put my arm around her legs, sniffing at her lap in the way I had sniffed at my mother's as a little boy every time I had pressed my head against her skirt; that's why all other women are at once familiar to me.

"Let me sleep alone," Tamara said, "I must be alone. We both need it. I'm used to my moments of solitude every day but here we've lived together. Then there has been Kustaa Mauri. And this knowledge that I've done something bad. Is there any remedy against it? I must have time to think, put my thoughts in order. It may take a day, two, or even a week, but I'll find an answer and next time I'll be a little wiser."

"More cautious?"

"Perhaps not more cautious, but wiser. Perhaps see more sides to the matter. I may act in the same way even then. Just think, if one lived three hundred years," she said, returning to her favorite theme, "—don't laugh, this has to do with relativity—if one lived for three hundred years, one would make mistakes for a hundred years, correct them for the next hundred, and for the last hundred years one would perhaps know how to live."

"Yes," I said, sniffing at her, "one would."

"Let me sleep alone."

I let her. I remembered how my mother weaned me, and purposely bit my nails to show them to Tamara in the morning.

We got letters now and then, and every day the local newspaper, which had been ordered specially for my moments alone and so that I should obtain as close a contact as possible with the intellectual life of the region. Gradually it began to seem vitally important to read the weather report every day, giving assurance that the hot spell was not just an aberration of the senses. In addition I read those articles of a general nature typical of the district, about the loneliness of the forest-fire watcher and the special characteristics of the bee, such as an abhorrence of sweat and alcohol. The best honey, they said, comes from rosebay, which was flowering everywhere now, dominating the landscape after the wild chervil. The long grass in the meadow began to turn yellow like grain. Undisturbed, ungrazed, and uncut, it had a luxurious look, enhanced by the larks which every now and then rose vertically from the grass, declaring to the whole world how great a joy it was to dwell away from mowing machines, rakes, and hoofs; and those small, pale gray, heart-shaped butterflies whose appearance I had awaited and which now rose in a cloud into the air when Tamara ran down to the shore, avoiding the spiders' webs spun over the path.

I could not of course avoid reading about various follies around the world, much as I would have liked to imagine living this summer outside time. In summer human cruelty seems even more incomprehensible than in winter. I am always aghast at the enormous activity of this lazy and comfort-loving species where evil is in question. Perhaps it is simply not yet accustomed to goodness, I reasoned in the loneliness of my room. Goodness is new to the human race; we have not yet found out all its uses, just as nuclear power has not yet been successfully harnessed for peaceful purposes. After all, man is not yet accustomed to food even in those parts where it is abundant; he crams too much of it into himself as if he were afraid it would end at any minute. It came into my mind that this assumption might be extended to cover property and income, official duties, even work. Just as acquiring excess property is set in question, one could ask whether it is right that some people grab all the work while others suffer from unemployment. Work too seems to tend to gather into the same hands. These thoughts came to me one day when I was reading in my room while Tamara and Kustaa Mauri held sway over the yard, the living room, and the kitchen, and although I had not really thought about my essay on the identity of the intelligentsia during this time, I decided to link this idea to it and made a note of it.

This puzzled me, for my social awakening occurred ages ago, at the time when I was overtaken by the physical state in which I now am. By identifying myself with the Left of that time I felt for the first time the joy of belonging to some group. I wrote some of my best things then, in a completely hopeless state, knowing nothing of what the future might hold in store for me. Then there followed a setback, a period when I was fed up with the whole business; for me who at that time was already beginning to experience everything verbally it was a terrible disappointment to notice the repetition of the same phrases, intelligent people caught up in reiterating the clumsy texts of the party offices, verbally talented individuals producing stillborn prose with the idea that "everything must be said so the man in the street can understand it," that art in itself is nothing. How they deceived their listeners. And what harm they did to themselves. And it went on. At this stage they began to call me a revisionist. I found out what revisionism really meant and admitted: True, I am a revisionist. I want to link new knowledge to feeling, and through it also to tradition, since without feeling no culture is created, and every new creed demands a new culture around it, its own culture, but it must always be linked to man's psyche, his deepest world of sensation, otherwise it will not live.

This essay I am thinking of will be interpreted as right wing like many other of my recent writings. It is depressing. But I do not want to make the easy decision and declare myself a leftist, for which perhaps I would be blessed. I must for some reason move, drag myself, in this most difficult way, so like martyrdom as it may seem, hobble, make false moves, because for me nothing else is possible. I do not understand how people manage to be born so complete. Let me express my standpoint only when I have been dead for three hundred years. Then I would believe I saw life sufficiently whole to be able to say something about it.

You may say that I have run away. So I have, and is it any wonder? The wonder to me is that so few have run away so far. The only thing I know is that I do not belong to any group. Love must be secret, says Tamara. I am a secret leftist, because I do not wish to identify with the intellectual Left, that nauseating crowd with no identity of its own. I am not a working chap. I am an invalid in this matter too, socially paralyzed.

* * *

I came to think that our present way of life was not perhaps the best possible for the remnants of my nerves. Something—use of time?—had been miscalculated, because I was quite obviously becoming irritable, a fault I did not normally have. Or maybe Tamara was neglecting me; did she in fact tell me anything anymore? At that moment she came in with an open letter in her hand.

"I've got a letter," she said, as if I had not seen it. "You can't guess who from."

"Where is Kustaa Mauri?" I said, for I thought he had arrived only a moment before.

"He only had time to drop by, and you know how I hate hurry. He was going to some dog trials. He's been training the dogs for a long time to follow a trail, which is very rare for Dobermans. But there seems to be no limit to his ambition. Whenever the dogs are there he gives me less attention and caresses me absent-mindedly, always with one eye on the dogs. Sometimes he's even shouted "down" or "here" in the middle of a kiss. And whenever he looks elsewhere the dogs bare their teeth at me."

"Well, life isn't easy for that man either." I took a more comfortable position in my chair and calmly prepared to sweat as I listened to Tamara's letter. "People should sweat freely and without embarrassment in summer at least," I said. "It's that opening of the ducts that you glorify so much, the purgative pleasure; it should occur without restraint and without burdening the mind. What a terrible strain to have to conceal one's natural functions. I remember a cheerful cousin on my mother's side who every summer allowed himself the right to fart freely and audibly. But by the end of August he began to practice closing the retentive muscles in order to get it under complete control before school started. It was a great psychological strain. And on my father's side there was a family who were famous not only for their great peaceableness, but also for the rare understanding they showed for each others' flatulence; the fact being that the whole family suffered from poor digestion and ate bicarbonate all day long. They could call each other from one room to another without opening their mouths, and because they were musical such concerts were said to be quite agreeable to hear."

"Do you want to hear this letter or not?" Tamara asked impatiently. "This is something new, but I've heard that story of yours a hundred times. Try and guess who it's from."

"Kustaa Mauri's wife."

"Silly. Why on earth would she write to me? She doesn't even know I exist. This is from our friend the knife grinder."

"How would he know we are here?"

"I gave our address of course. And he doesn't know we are here, he thinks I'm here alone. He was so sad when I said I'd be away for several weeks that I suggested he write to me. He has deep philosophical ideas, he could put them down on paper and perhaps get a response. He was excited by the idea, his face really lit up and got red. People miss a lot when they stop writing letters. Not that I've ever been a letter writer myself."

The letter was a ready-folded unit decorated with a color print showing a Finnish landscape. I had never seen such a thing before. On the address side there was a fragment of a waterfall running into quiet waters, and on the reverse side a sunset over a lake scene, and when the letter was opened one was rewarded with four smaller scenes, in color too: one of Koli's highest point, another of Punkaharju's topmost branch, a third of the Inkoo archipelago, and the fourth from the shore of some soon-to-be polluted lake, seen through the boughs of weeping birches. And beyond these six lakes and mountains one human heart opened up to another. Frans Siltanen wrote:

Dear Friend,

Greetings to my good Friend from here in the Capital as I promised to write to You there in the summer

*cottage So I am asking how are tricks fine of course,
You hear the cuckoo there and the birds singing though
otherwise it must be quiet. I promised to write a filo
sofic, but now the old swede is not really in form so I
cannot write any deep thoughts now, perhaps You will
forgive me now for my emptiness and dullness. I would
like to suggest we use first names to give more go to my
letter if, You do not mind and if my poor old nut sometime cracks a thought then it would be liberating to
complexes of the Soul, I would like to open it to You. I
ask if there is a very run down summer cottage there
abouts, I would come and paint a picture of it, it would
be an interesting subject, and I would ask to talk
privately with You, that would be interesting too, so that
we could open ourselves to each other. I am alone in
this Valley of Tears, as I was ill a lot and my youth went
in drinking I take life more serious and dignified now,
when only a little of life is left. I greet You in all friendly-
ness with a very sincere Heart and with all respects
Goodbye*

*Frans Siltanen
Knife Blunter*

PS. My address is still the same Peace Haven 4.

Tamara turned the letter over, looking carefully at each
scene separately.

"One must always look at the pictures carefully, a post-card
sender spends a lot of time choosing the card, it conveys the
unconscious greetings of his mind. He has placed us of course
in his mind in all these scenes, on that uncomfortable-looking
rock and in the spray of those falls. I'm ashamed that I never
got on first-name terms with him before. But he always looked
at me so meaningfully, I didn't dare, I thought there should
be some sort of distance between us—especially after that
courting business."

158

"Ahaa. You haven't told me about that. Why not?"

"Oh, you know, one's tongue gets tired sometimes. It was all very nice. I was making some mead on the balcony—I meant to have a little party for our group, it was only a few days from May Day. Frans came and asked if there was anything to sharpen. I never say there isn't, because once he woke me up at seven o'clock on a Sunday morning and I answered angrily that there never is at that time of the morning, and then I felt so bad I got dressed and ran after him in the street and pushed the two marks he would have earned into his hand. I remembered it was Sunday and there was no chance of earning anything anywhere; even the Salvation Army was closed. That's how we got to know each other, and he attached himself to me. Where was I now?"

"Where he came just before May Day."

"Yes, well, I gave him knives and scissors, and generally he sharpened them in the yard or on the stairs, but I'd already asked him in several times and now I said: 'Come up here on the balcony and I'll give you some mead.' And we sipped the mead and he filed away at my scissors and started to ask me all sorts of things, where I worked and what my husband did. 'I don't have a husband,' I said. 'Why not try me?' he asked, examining the scissors for sharpness. 'Oh no, I'm a bad-tempered woman, men can't stand me.' 'I'm easygoing,' he said. And a few days later he appeared all dressed up, clean and combed—actually he's always very tidy—and he was sort of swaggering and sure of himself. He'd decided to try again in earnest. 'Anything to sharpen?' he said carelessly, a cigarette in his left hand. It was a lovely evening, the light from the window on the stairs shone in, and phrases from the Bible came into my mind. But unfortunately I was in a hurry to go to a meeting, and in the rush took out the usual two marks. As soon as I did I saw how deeply it insulted him. He put the money in his pocket and went away, his back bent; it's in the back that you see humiliation. And I felt terrible all evening, was quarrelsome at the meeting, and the necessity of a change in the attitude of the staff was pointed out to me once more. But imagine, he forgave me and turned up again a month later. I let him make new tips for my nail scissors; it took a long time and made amends for my treatment of him. I made some coffee and he told me his life story. We've had a long and varying relationship, with all kinds of phases. Then once when I was absolutely fed up with him I got the idea of sending him to you."

"Many thanks," I said. "I didn't know that you two had such an emotional history behind you. As a matter of fact when I think about it more carefully, he is my only rival. He has all the prerequisites. Can write letters. Is faithful and clinging, offers the possibility of continuity. Is not married. Is one of those rare, valuable, unattached men. Does not drink anymore, smokes moderately because of his ulcer. Has a bit of the artist in him and, above all, is an ex-alcoholic, an admirable personage, a strong character."

"Yes, yes," said Tamara, "but Frans isn't the only one. You have another rival, who may be even more of an invalid than you."

She dug another letter out of her pocket.

"This is beginning to be monotonous."

"Don't say anything yet, listen first: 'Dear Tamara, you certainly don't remember me any longer, as I was only in the ward for quite a short time and we did not have much to do with each other. But I looked at no one but you.' "

"Promising." (My spirits were distinctly beginning to rise.)

"Don't keep interrupting all the time," yelled Tamara, putting the day's second love letter on her knee. Then she forgot the letter and started reading her own thoughts: "Imagine the enormous potentials for loving that are entirely unused. And they resist being smothered, whatever the conditions."

"And think if one could learn to control them scientifically. You press a button and they spark up in both parties at

160

exactly the same moment. And for a beautiful ending one should develop a legal form of euthanasia."

"Don't keep interrupting," Tamara screamed, and I realized that in addition to my many admirable qualities she also expected muteness.

Tamara went back to her letter: "I think you are such a warm, tender, and open person' "—I cleared my throat, making her hesitate for a moment and—believe it or not—blush a little too—" 'and I have been warmed by your ideas, especially those you put forward at the wards' general discussion evening on sexual subjects.' . . . Do you want to hear this or not?" she demanded, now clearly embarrassed; reading aloud has a touch of exhibitionism, and she already knew the rest of the letter's contents.

"I am a mere audiovisual erection."

"You could read this yourself."

"Of course, but two fond hearts together and listening to the loved one . . ."

"Balls."

"Is that what it says there?"

She was herself once more and continued: " 'I am now approaching you with the intention of getting you to advise me about books that give a thorough description of sex life, coitus and the preliminaries. The books are expensive to buy and one cannot get such books from libraries. You may not remember but I will mention that I cannot go to a bookshop, and must order by mail everything I read. What writer describes how a man licks a woman's labia and clitoris, breasts, thighs, behind, and everything else, and how a woman sucks a man's penis and licks his testicles? Novels and stories should describe those wonderful preludes and everything connected with them as well as sexual intercourse. Love should be a spiritual and physical whole even in novels. I am not interested in books about positions only. I remember you do not like the words cunt, quim, cock, prick, and fuck.

161

I like them. To me they are beautiful and tender, but so are the words labia, vagina, clitoris, and penis. I remember that they seemed to you either medical terms or bad nicknames, but you do not have the same background as I do. There are many people like me. Everything to do with sex and its description is beautiful to me, lesbian and homosexual too. People should be candid with each other . . ."

Tamara's nose had started to run and she pulled a handkerchief out of her pocket and blew it thoroughly, a little too long for the time of year; perhaps hay fever struck her at that moment. Then she went on without looking at me:

" '. . . and touch each other, be tender with one another and tolerant. And should not be hurt, but experiment with new things, be renewed, be open to influences. Why do so few artists dare give an open, passionate, detailed, uninhibited description of sexual activities? Especially women. I cannot understand how sex in general can be experienced negatively, as still happens. It is after all one of those rare things from which everyone can obtain joy, pleasure, and satisfaction. Isn't that true? And independently of age, wealth, or beauty— illness is the only exception. Descriptions written by men are often boastful and crude and they put women down. Very few men dare describe their feelings at all. Please, dear Tamara, write and answer me. What do you think about my ideas, do you approve of them?' "

"But the letter still goes on," I said as Tamara began to fold it up. "What else does it say?"

"Oh, nothing much."

"Yes it does, don't stop there. Otherwise this is like coitus interruptus, which you know I detest."

Tamara blew her nose. "He says that I am a very charming, very tender, and very intelligent person, and is quite warmed at the thought of me. So now you know."

I began to laugh. It is very rare for Tamara to be embarrassed by praise. On the contrary, she was in the habit of

162

saying: "I feel depressed. I haven't been praised for a long time."

"And now you obviously intend to add modesty to your other virtues," I said.

"You're monstrous, a monster," she said, and true enough, in her eyes were real tears. "This man writes a wise letter about an important matter and you sit there laughing. One would have thought this applied to you particularly."

"Oh, is it a man writing?"

"How would I know—it may be the same kind of neuter supersexualist as you are. I don't remember the person. I don't have the slightest idea of what the person looks like. But there's a man's name here at the end."

"Perhaps it's that telephone masturbator, that underclothes fetishist."

"Could be, but I don't really believe it. Incidentally, I've asked him not to call so often. It always drains me."

She rubbed her temples. I knew she would soon come to me and lay her head on my knees. I enjoyed waiting, my self-assurance grew, overtaking the knife grinder, the telephone fetishist, and even this literary erotomaniac, and they all seemed to merge into one embodiment of phallic completeness directed by my supreme spirit. Tamara came, spread her hair over my knees, like a Doberman pinscher under an Afghan's coat. The voice is the voice of Jacob, but the hands are the hands of Esau, I thought.

I twisted my fingers in her hair and felt the hard, hot skull throbbing against the sensitive skin of my fingertips.

"What would it really be like with you?" she said, rubbing her head against my knees. "I'm beginning to want to have your verbal orgasms too, maybe they would be soothing. Anyway, we're becoming inveterate babblers. These letters bother me. I can't divide myself anymore. Couldn't you answer them?"

"Immoral. But of course we can always talk about it.

There's still a postscript to this one," I said, taking the letter from her hand, massaging her scalp with my other hand, feeling its mobility.

On the last page was written: "P.S. What does the French word 'con' mean?"

"There you are," I said triumphantly. "Have I not always said that languages should be taught from love stories and sex guides? The entire dynamics of eroticism could be directed to the service of mankind through education and science. A new philosophy could be created: paneroticism, quimism, and prickism, with the common name of priquimism. The psychology of erotic language would be the central field of study. Actually I tried to put all this into practice in your case, and the result really isn't bad at all."

Having once got started I raved on, associations were born like new veins in gangrenous flesh, forgotten folk words and expressions flooded into my mind, ancient runes of the Finnish people welled forth from my lips; I remembered long passionate verses from the Koran and the Song of Solomon; a nursery rhyme that began "Tit tit titty"; a tale about a boy who penetrated a hole in a tree and begat flying squirrels; even beautiful old terms in Sanskrit. In the end I spoke a new, strange language that resounded and rolled.

"Does it make you feel better?" Tamara asked.

I awoke from my linguistic trance.

"Yes, in a way it does, I must admit."

"Then promise that you'll make me a list of French words to send the writer of this letter, so he can start learning according to your method."

"Well, wait till we get back to town, I do not remember them by heart," I said, still up in the clouds.

So we decided when we got back to town to prepare for the writer of the letter as complete a list as possible of French sexual vocabulary with Finnish equivalents, as far as we were able within the limits of our knowledge and a reasonable amount of trouble. In addition we spent that evening drawing up from memory a bibliography of pornographic and erotic literature for emergency use, and talked for a long time about which of them we would recommend to a person with such high standards. We decided to write to the knife grinder that we had not seen any run-down cottages here at all, and were in any case soon going back to town, but first-name terms were agreed upon as of now.

Tamara suddenly looked at me searchingly.

"Funny that you don't seem to feel a need to identify now," she said. "Why is that? Wouldn't this be a welcome change for you?"

I had to think; it was true enough.

"Frans is too familiar," I said. "And then he has that red nose. I must re-create your men in my imagination, decide what they are like. Now I see why I avoided seeing Kustaa Mauri. Besides, you do not like Frans in that way, and that is the decisive point. And this biblioerotomaniac is too much like me; I don't want to identify with my shadow. I'm sure he's an artist, a specialist in orgasms of the imagination, world champion of subconscious coupling."

"Be careful. I felt sympathy for him because he resembled you. Soon he'll begin to irritate me for the same reasons you do."

"Intellectuals' identity," I said, "imbeciles' impotency, impotents' introversion, intriguers' anamorphosis, amaranthists' assimilation."

"Stop it," Tamara shouted, her hands over her ears, "stop it!"

"I have to cool off. Amoral varient's dejaculation."

"There should be no mail in summer. My compassion is on vacation," Tamara said. "How I long for him. It's terrible to see him so briefly."

Kustaa Mauri's absence upset Tamara in the extreme. They had not been apart for a single day since he had begun to visit her in the country. The recent hustle and bustle over the letters was a happy respite, the moment of rest after which the body and soul can flare up into a new flame. It had been Sunday morning when Tamara sat on her knees between his legs and took him in hand, like churning butter in an old-fashion dasher churn.

"The sperm flew all over my neck and breasts, I laughed and took the rest in my mouth—he penetrated me in every way."

"Which Sunday was this then?"

"What does that matter? One Sunday's as good as another. Any Sunday you like. Our Sunday. The Sunday morning of my life. It's only a pity it's past."

Time was kneaded back and forth in our hands, its plastic dimensions totally unable to meet our demands, in which joy was vital.

166

"Well, can he do it by himself now?" I once asked.

"Yes, he can. I taught him. Guiding him by the hand. Only now he's become addicted to my hands and wants them like a child a candy. But this is evidently my fate. Either they want to stick their fingers into me or they only want my hand. And as far as I'm concerned I wouldn't care if hands didn't exist."

She laughed. I shook my head.

"You have chosen badly again. You should have looked for a man without hands. What about the armless raker?"

"Even he has those stumps. And the problem isn't solved as long as I have these hands of my own. There's something wrong with this species when it's become so estranged from the natural way of making love. I'm beginning to be thought odd. I'll soon be ashamed of my limitations. I blush when I have to ask 'Couldn't you just put it where it belongs?'; some of them don't even understand what that means, they're surprised and look at me with eyes like saucers. They think it's some new position they don't know anything about yet. And then I have to explain and show how old-fashioned I am."

"Are you talking about Kustaa Mauri?"

"No, about men in general. Kustaa Mauri is so dependent on my hands that I can always guide him where he belongs."

"I understand."

"Afterward he's always surprised that he enjoyed that too. He calls me his phallic phase. It's a sign of high spiritual maturity, apparently."

This conversation took place on the lakeshore, where in the absence of Kustaa Mauri I had taken the trouble to drag myself. It was a warm day; the hot spell continued. The juniper trees had died in the whole clearing; in spite of their hardiness they can't take excessive drought or cold. The leafy trees glittered in the sun like metal. Grasshoppers had won from the birds the right to be heard; it seemed like a turning point in summer. Tamara had been swimming and brought me a long-stemmed water lily. I cut it to what I guessed was a suitable length and pressed it carefully into her. The flower remained visible like an ornamental plug and a green dragon-fly hovered over it for a moment.

"One thing I don't understand is why people are so crazy about sixty-nine. As far as I'm concerned the whole idea is to get the right places against each other."

"Quite," I said, moving the water lily gently back and forth.

Her body became tense as if listening and she stretched her arms above her head in order to be quite relaxed. For some reason her patients came to her mind.

"I know they masturbate and it's quite appropriate; people must have some sort of sex life. But they do it violently and are disgusted with themselves. I've told them one should treat oneself kindly and tenderly, caress oneself carefully and sympathetically, accepting that this time there's nothing better available."

I picked up from the grass a little bird's feather, maybe a meadow pipit's, and tickled her with it, seeking the most sensitive spot among the hairs. On the lake a motor boat went by; the people in it were scanning the shores with binoculars—a peculiar bunch. The water lily began to stir by itself as if rocked by an undercurrent.

"One day I'll stuff you with little apples, I'll count how many paradise apples will go in. It might be a world record."

She was beautiful. Her whole body was covered with tiny drops of perspiration, it started to tremble and finally contracted as if a nerve had been touched with a probe; it happened many times over and I loved these involuntary spasms. I pushed my fingers into her and felt how she was throbbing. Then she squeezed them hard with repeated contractions.

"Do you feel this movement?" she said, her eyes closed.

"Yes."

"It means hello my friend, a very good and nice day to you.

How are you? Lovely to meet you. Best regards. Bye-bye. Keep well. Hope you come again."

I lay down beside her on the blanket and sniffed the water lily. I felt a pain in my heart and was quiet for a while. The earth seemed to be rocking beneath me, something spun at high speed in my head, my ears had suddenly gone deaf as if artillery had been fired somewhere near. Little motes floated before my eyes. An erotic experience, when it was really successful, always flung me to the brink of consciousness, against its walls, to the uttermost regions of my element, as if I were being punished because I had experienced a joy which in theory was no longer within my scope. Physically hazardous as this experience is, it supported the idea that I had always had: that love, though rarely fatal, is still a question of life and death. That is the reason for the sense of happening connected with love, and the feeling that everything else is peripheral, sheer nonsense.

"It was only a clitoral orgasm, which was reflected in the vagina," Tamara explained.

"Is there a difference between them?" I managed to ask.

"It's a disputed point. The sexologists argue about it."

"There's a big difference. The clitoral orgasm comes from exciting the erectile organ of the vulva, and anybody can do it for themselves. But the vaginal orgasm follows from the rubbing of the deeper regions, in a place you can't localize, and for me at any rate this can be done only by a man, and it totally drains me. Still, they're both good and interesting. It's a question of taste, which you prefer. Yes, and then there are all kinds of variations and combinations. Endlessly."

"I'm going to keep this water lily," I said, revolving the flower against the sky, "I'll dry it."

"No," exclaimed Tamara, horrified, "no, I can't stand anything mummified. I should have thought you'd chose your symbols better."

She snatched the water lily from my hand and threw it far into the long grass. I had to be satisfied with that.

"When is Kustaa Mauri coming again?" I said, putting my arm around her; her skin was so hot it almost burned, she was brown all over.

"I don't know. He hasn't consented to say. Doesn't know himself, maybe. Once I said that in autumn I'd like to know beforehand when we'll meet. I can't stand waiting. But he was horrified by the idea and was silent the rest of the day. I don't know whether I dare to suggest it to him again. I have my pride too. He behaved as if I'd recommended life imprisonment."

"Pity."

"I've already told him once that though I've been humble with him, I'm not really," Tamara said.

To tell the truth I had been wondering in my moments alone about this particular matter, but it had never come into my head when we were together, for understandable reasons.

"Why are you so humble then?"

"If only I knew. He assures me he is reliable, but his attitude arouses in me an unbearable insecurity. I'm not used to reliable people. And I want to keep him, this man I want to keep. I'd give anything to maintain this relationship. I'm even ready to be faithful without demanding anything of him. Besides at bottom I am faithful by nature"—"Really?" I asked, surprised—"it's just that I've never had the chance to fulfill that side of me."

In her agitation she turned on her stomach and sent off an ant that had lingered in front of her. I stroked the hollows in her back.

"Yes," I admitted, "it is as simple as that."

"Don't make fun. Have you forgotten what waiting and uncertainty and giving up feel like? Every time we say good-bye I give up my rights to him and I never know whether he'll come again, every time I fall into loneliness and then I come to you. And every time he comes after all or calls me, I receive him anew as a gift, I open myself again to joy and gratitude. It's hard. Do you understand now that one can

170

long for dull gray everyday security? It would be a wonderful change for me, though I know it would kill me in a short time, as overgrowth of vegetation kills a pond and its fish."

True, I thought, and then said it aloud: that I lived as it were on the minus side, where good sense said that there was nothing more to expect, in no-man's-time, where I'd had to learn to renounce so thoroughly that it had acquired a certain value; still, there are still more wretched creatures than me, I said encouragingly. "Of course you upset this negative balance," I said, stroking her back and brushing away the horse flies, "but in a very pleasant way."

"I wish you a profound sorrow in love. It would mature you as a human being, deepen and broaden you, do you good in every way."

She was really amusing. I laughed but the thought shot through me of what my life would be if nobody ever talked nonsense to me again and made me laugh right down to my insensible depths.

"You should say this to Kustaa Mauri; it seems to me that he's the one who needs it. He probably doesn't even realize that an absolutely wonderful thing has happened to him."

"I have said it. And he realizes all right. He's often said afterward: 'Unbelievable, you probably haven't the slightest idea what this means to me.' And I don't know, because I can't imagine him otherwise. He has his own pattern of behavior, his own conditions, and I happen to fit in. But he just laughs at unhappy love. Everyone laughs at it. Yet it's one of the most painful and humiliating feelings there are."

I suddenly heard the woodpecker calling in the pines below the rocks. Tamara heard it too, for she raised herself up with her arms and listened. The agitated squawk of distress was heard again.

"It's come back," she yelled. "The woodpecker has come back. Or one of them. Can you hear? They're alive."

If it had come back, it was only to go away again. The sound could no longer be heard.

171

"When the young woodpecker learns to fly, it rarely returns to the nest," I thought wise to explain.

"What do you mean by that?" Tamara said, sitting up and looking at me with flashing eyes.

I assured her that I by no means always spoke in metaphors, much as I loved them.

Nevertheless I did think of Kustaa Mauri. I could have embraced him, congratulated him, shaken his hand, slapped him on the shoulder.

He had met happiness and intended quietly to pat it in passing. But it had kicked him so hard that he was still licking his wounds.

Days had gone by, but no news of Kustaa Mauri.

"The dogs missed out in the contest and he's sorrowing over that, or then he's stayed in town to attend the Doberman seminars," Tamara said.

The first days she seemed to be deliberately resting, but in the evenings she always began to listen. Really, I thought, what an unreasonable burden love is, high as my opinion of that feeling is normally.

"Did you ever talk about things in general?" I asked.

"Oh, we talked about everything, though of course it couldn't help being a bit fragmentary. Everyone should have a second life for talking. He was surprised we had such an erotic relationship—he blamed me for it of course, said he'd expected something else. All my life I'd been waiting for a man who would love me for my brains, and when one turned up I'd already given up hope that they could exist."

"Men or brains?"

"Maybe he thinks I've already gone back to town."

"Well, you have got your telephone answering service there."

"That would just annoy him."

You watch the telephone like a dog watching a bag of sausages, I felt like saying, but hadn't the heart to. I knew that she was conscious of all the shades of the situation. I simply said: "Protect yourself." "I do," she answered, "but to protect myself I must search carefully through all the crannies of my mind, get to know myself, see what bottomless reserves a person has against pain—one shouldn't be frightened of them or avoid them but explore them. This is what 'Know thyself' means. It means: 'Become familiar with yourself, acknowledge yourself, and you'll be in control, live in harmony with your own dangers.' I know this by heart because this is what I say to everyone I have to do with in my work."

"Do they understand what you are talking about?"

"Nearly all of them understand and many have thought the same themselves, even experienced it, without any encouragement. And quite a few realize it afterward, come and tell me that it stayed in their mind, and that's the knowledge they really came to find. But all our upbringing and way of life leads us away from ourselves, always we 'must,' always we're in a hurry. Here in the country there's a different time, just like in space, here there's natural time still, the plants' and animals' time—for them summer's the whole of existence. We go back rejuvenated to the city and the hurry and the press of people. Or perhaps compared with that mini-life we're eternal, like great planets, and ancient and wise when we leave here."

I was not really able to follow the track of her thoughts, but I considered this resorting to a micro- and macrocosmos an alarming sign. She always relied on astronomy and biochemistry, with a tendency toward metaphysics, when she was trying to relate typical unpleasant knowledge about human life to the natural system. I must admit that she sometimes succeeded in creating a quite credible structure. As long as UFOs and the more concrete manifestations of parapsychology did not enter into the conversation, I had no objection to this kind of thought marathon. On the contrary, it struck me that astronomy might easily take the place of religion for intellectuals, and create both stability, extraterrestrial dimensions, and a sense of relativity. Besides, it would be a sufficiently concrete counterweight to sociology, that great science of our time.

Tamara went to the mailbox.

"No letters?" I asked.

"Of course not. Who would write in this heat?"

"Not even a card?"

"No. And if you're hinting at Kustaa Mauri, he never writes letters, let alone cards."

"Ah," I said, "then I must add that information to his personal dossier."

She read the paper carefully and I waited, my basket chair creaking nervously.

"Are there many notices of deaths? Did you remember the drownings and car accidents? And all the murders and so on?"

She threw the paper in my face and left the room, reluctantly because the telephone happened to be in this room.

"And the ads and the miscellaneous column?" I shouted after her, trying to get the paper into shape again.

"I left them for you," she shouted in through the window, "they're meant for people like you—ex-man seeks ex-woman."

I saw how she ran down to the shore, threw off her few clothes as she reached the jetty, and splashed in. She swam with long strokes toward the open water, diving every so often. Her head looked very small as she went farther away across the glittering lake and vanished from sight for long periods in the sun-drenched waves. Who was the fellow who claimed anyone could enjoy the spectacle of a sinking ship as long as he was on shore? I would gladly have shared my enjoyment with him, even adding a few metaphysical

175

musings. I also thought, quite simply, the devil take that Kustaa Mauri. Did he have to resort to making a woman wait humbly instead of honestly discussing the situation with her, as any adult would about an affair between adults? (When, where, and who might have experienced such an affair for this myth to have originated? Or is it only a delusion born of our need for the absolute, that cancer of the human mind?) After all he was merely a poor, inexperienced creature, paralyzed by the sacred laws of marriage, a sluggish civil servant never conscious of the more subtle nuances of the human heart, who counted even this success simply as an addition to his list of merits or, marginally, as supplementary information about his favorite hobbies.

I understood too why rulers of old married their mistresses to their war chiefs and advisers. In my personal realm the princess had to get this ass; the psychology of fairy tales never fails.

Tamara still had a defiant look when she came in, her hair wet, her eyes red from diving.

I reproached her.

"When you rush into the lake like that, you break in one second those elaborate spiders' webs built with such great trouble all along the path and which we preserved all summer. Only yesterday evening when the dew was rising I was admiring them. And as I remember we have respected them as one of those marvels of nature where function and aesthetic quality form an undeniable harmony." I used my sorrowful learned voice, which I do when the occasion arises.

To my surprise this had the desired effect on her. She flopped down into a chair quite exhausted, her defiance gone, and sat there rubbing her face, which now openly reflected depression, unhappiness, and weariness.

"I forgot," she said. "How could I forget them? I've been the one to safeguard them all the time. But still you don't need to speak to me in that voice, like the whining of a lay preacher who's fallen in love with an entomologist.

176

"I must be in love with him," she continued.

I was so surprised that I almost fell out of my chair. "Hasn't that been clear right from the start?" I managed to stutter.

"Not at all. I've said that I love him and through him the whole human race, that inferior species I ought to despise. But I've never once claimed or suspected I was in love with him. That's quite another matter. Falling in love is an acute occurrence in the central nervous system, like a stroke. If in addition to loving you still fall in love, it's like a new acute disease striking a chronic invalid. One's condition becomes critical. Anyway it feels like that for oneself and those closely concerned."

I guessed that in this picture of disease I represented one closely concerned, so I decided to be brave and continued: "But is the order not generally the other way around, does the disease not begin by being acute and only later gradually become chronic?"

"That's right, generally. But when everything happens the other way around, like now, the situation is much more serious. That's very rare, it's true. I've never experienced it before."

"But how is it that you now," I fumbled, "why is it that this time you . . . ?"

"I don't know. Of course there's my own basic state of mind and there're previous experiences, the whole background, and there's this deviating from my previous unsettled affairs, when I knew beforehand how they would turn out . . ."

"But supposing everything does turn out in the same way?" I interrupted her tenderly, trying to slip this idea into her mind for the first time, unnoticed.

"No," she said violently. "I couldn't stand that. I've gone into this affair just because I expected it to be better than all the rest, different from earlier ones and from affairs generally. I consciously decided to change types to save myself from

177

now on. I've had my fill of being alone again, empty like a deflated balloon. I can't stand this eternal collapse."

"I can see that," I said, trying to make my voice sound sympathetic, as if I understood and accepted—that was obviously my real role in this business as in other, similar ones. I noted with satisfaction, however, that she used the word "affair" for the first time. Surely that must mean something, if nothing more, a good effort to demystify the whole thing.

"When I hear the wind I think that he's whistling from somewhere near on his way here."

"Where can you hear the wind whistling? In this heat there's not even a leaf stirring."

"It's there, just listen quietly."

And true enough, when I sharpened my hearing to the uttermost, I could hear through the chirping of the crickets how a delicate ripple of wind moved through the open window from time to time, and whimpered almost soundlessly as it passed through the narrow crack between window frame and wall.

"Do you really have to strain yourself to listen to that?" I said, with unforgivable lack of understanding; I was not especially prone to finesses just now. Rather I was disposed to a great general thankfulness that she was sitting here before me, disheartened but not drowned. "Frankly those crickets make such a racket that you can't hear anything else. Every now and again I get a crazy feeling that I am shut up in a watch shop full of watches ticking at different speeds."

"I do try as hard as I can not to listen, I've even eaten lots of crisp bread just so the crunching would stop me listening, but afterward I always feel the phone must have rung at that moment."

"Now I believe it is serious."

"And in the evening I think I see him there under the spruce tree, like in a dream, always coming toward the house but never arriving. And going to the shop I've seen him dozens of times and each time like magic he changes into a complete stranger before my eyes."

I felt that she really wanted to get it off her chest now, and I let her go on without interrupting, describing all the different ways in which she imagined seeing or hearing her loved one's approach and thought she recognized his voice: in the burble of water, the hum of a fly, the grumble of a stomach, the rocking of the rosebay, in stones and tree trunks; even a gnarled spruce tree was a reminder of Kustaa Mauri, the clouds in the sky formed the shape of his profile lying with closed eyes; the bed cried for him and the old spring mattress invited with its sighs other sounds of lovemaking; Tamara was going to sleep on the floor from now on, unless Kustaa Mauri sent some news of himself very soon.

"What about me?" I plucked up courage to say. "There's still me left."

"Oh yes," she said, and the conversation ended there.

The days slipped by with disconcerting speed but with nothing to show for them: Tamara was angry at the heat, grumbled at the heavy rainless clouds, was indignant when for a change it rained gently; if only there were real lightning, thunder, and pouring rain, a high wind, whipping the flowers to the ground, beating down the grass, rending the trees, demolishing this pompous villa so that no stone remained on stone.

"Now I know the origin of man's rage to destroy," Tamara said. "I wish some upheaval of nature would devastate this place, I can't stand it anymore."

As she had threatened, she had slept on the floor, spread under her one of her precious, sperm-spattered sheets, turned and twisted there all night, read until late some literature about Doberman pinschers that Kustaa Mauri had brought her sometime, made her limbs sore on the hard floor; she had even been surprised by a cramp and had suffered it alone, without any help.

I was confused and puzzled. It seemed to me unreasonable and illogical to make my presence so valueless; nothing like this had ever happened before. I too longed for and cursed at Kustaa Mauri in my helplessness; that damned castrated cock, as I called him in my mind, that poor bloody paralyzed creature, spoiling someone else's summer and life. And I was ready to bless him whenever he would condescend to appear.

The harsh scream of the woodpeckers could be heard now and again, sometimes from the hill, sometimes from the woods by the road. At first this made Tamara jump with joy, and I saw how pleasure tried to surface, brightening for a moment the expression on her face.

"It's a good sign," she said, "they didn't go away for good after all. They're still going around in these parts, they miss this place."

Then one evening there was a sound as if a woodpecker were knocking on the wall, kindly cleaning the house of those beetles that had bothered me all the summer with their patter and their flights that ended in tumbling to the floor.

"That's a bad sign, it means sorrows," Tamara announced gloomily. "I detest those spiders too, don't you think there are especially many of them this summer? They too just wait and wait, everywhere's full of this clinging web of waiting."

I considered it, however, a favorable sign that she did at least speak, fret, and rage, hurl herself from place to place, break dishes—nothing seemed to stay in her hands—batter her limbs against the furniture, burn her knuckles on the stove, cut her fingers when she should have been cutting bread. Every day she packed to leave for town, but did not make the final decision; her holiday was not yet over. She would clearly have liked to be in two places at once, in case Kustaa Mauri should have taken it into his head to meet her in either of them; this mood made the situation even more humiliating.

I pointed this out to her. She leaned on the table, bit at

181

the skin around her thumbnail, and was so sincerely sorrowful-looking that I would right away have maneuvered myself over to her and put my arm around her, even adopted the role of grandfather, if only it would had helped and I had been permitted. But she could not stand me closer than six feet from her, as she precisely decreed. From my point of view the situation was a dead end too; I was denied my essential function to her, on which our relation rested.

"True," she said, tearing away with her teeth such a large strip of flesh from the nail root that her thumb began to bleed; she needed a Band-Aid and I went off to look for one. "You're right. Everything depends on how you take it. If I had remained cool, the whole affair wouldn't have any special importance. But I can't help feeling that I've been made a fool of. This is injustice, d'you hear?"

"Yes," I shouted from the medicine cupboard in the bedroom. "Keep talking, I can hear you."

"This is unjust," she said, raising her voice. "It's not right to treat me like this. I've always been fair and open. Not a word, not an explanation, not even the pretense of a conclusion. He could have said: 'Wait for me two weeks, two months, two years, I'll come back then.' And I would have answered: 'All right, I'll wait.' It's as if he'd known that this is just what hurts me."

"Oh yes, he's known it all right; in this game people always learn to know what hurts most." The Band-Aid was in my hand.

"Aren't you ashamed," she said, pulling her thumb away and not letting me bind it. "All you do is turn the knife in the wound instead of consoling me."

"I thought it was an awl this time."

She laughed dismally like a parody of a tragic heroine, but put out her thumb to be bandaged, first licking the blood from it. She looked at me for a moment in contradiction to her words, a glimmer of humor in the corner of her eye like the last sign of life in the gaze of a drowning man, and this

182

made me understand more clearly than before how unhappy she was, possessed by her own—perhaps causeless—despair.

"Do you actually know what an awl is like?" she said. "It's for making a hole in the thickest and toughest leather, where more developed tools aren't any use at all."

"Are you hinting at the daggers of speech?" I improvised, and just managed to make her laugh.

"Imagine," she said, a little more cheerfully, "as a child I thought that languish meant the same as to have sexual intercourse, and I had the idea that languishing was something terribly secret and permitted only to adults."

"An interesting linguistic contamination," I said. "Did it also perhaps have some spiritual equivalent?"

Tamara thought about this; I was pleased to have turned her thoughts elsewhere.

"Maybe. I remember at some stage wondering why people seemed to go in for such a sad thing so enthusiastically."

A confession like this might have been a triumph for linguistic psychology, but for understandable reasons I was not able at that moment to enjoy it wholeheartedly, although I did make a brief entry in my notebook to be added later to the archives for more detailed consideration.

"Perhaps from then on I've been afraid that I'll be rejected, maybe even before that," Tamara said, suddenly becoming interested. "Or perhaps an already existing fear gave the word this significance. And I always have been rejected, that's true, and I've never got used to it. People can't stand me."

I could have said one or two things about this; pointed out that she was not one of the easiest people to get along with, but I contented myself with reminding her that people turned to her to the point of dependence, and that her profession bore witness against what she said.

"Yes, it's odd. If only they knew how helpless I am myself. Perhaps they stick to me because they sense that I know this helplessness personally. They're, as it were, liberated when I describe it to them and everything tallies. It's as if I take on their problems. It's a strange feeling. Whose suffering am I now bearing?—actually I myself have no real reason to suffer. But someone is suffering and all the susceptible people sense it as if they were receiving radio waves. Or else suffering is approaching and I'm tasting it in advance."

"That's not possible." I continued the conversation for therapeutic reasons, although in my opinion it was already slipping toward those more extreme metaphysical absurdities that only aroused nausea in me. "Think how much suffering there is in the world, always and everywhere, even at this moment, constantly. People would not have time to do anything else if they started to bear all that, as you say."

"No, they don't have time, they can't manage it. They're driven to the limit, to the point of breaking down. Some break down, some manage to carry on for a while, more or less."

"So you don't believe people can be helped?"

"Yes, they can be helped. Even suffering is helping. It's the taking part in sorrow, admitting it's justified, that gives spiritual strength and direction. People can't go on without sympathy. And people who suffer together are ready to share everything. Oh yes, that time will come, but perhaps there won't be a single sane person to enjoy it."

"Everything I have experienced with you and everything you say would be easier to understand if you would only tell me, briefly, everything about yourself, your background, and earlier life. You started studying rather late."

"No. I haven't tried to find out anything about you, except what has been necessary for practical reasons. And what I've said is true—there aren't any secrets in my life, except love, which has to be secret, and even that I don't keep secret from you. Nothing fateful happened to me and I hate the idea of you starting to explain me in the light of my past, however right you may be. I want you to take me as I am now."

She laughed for the first time in days and in my relief I

thanked God as I realized that the conversation had brightened her up and she had completely forgotten Kustaa Mauri. Evening quiet seemed for the first time in ages to be spreading its wings over our dwelling, and the plaintive cooing of a wood pigeon emphasized this feeling, like the signal of an armistice.

"Just between us two I'm so abnormally ordinary that I feel quite ashamed," she declared enthusiastically. "An ordinary person is a rarity and seems quite exceptional among all those peculiar people the world is full of. I've so often bumped into other people's peculiarities that I've learned to appear sufficiently odd to pass unnoticed. I just want to be like breathing, like air, that's all."

Pleased though I was at the turn our conversation had taken, I could not resist taking the opportunity to ask with apparent indifference:

"What about your son?"

But Tamara was not startled by the question as I had feared; she said calmly:

"We go our own ways now. But we'll become friends again when he's forty."

"You'll be over sixty then," I said.

"Yes, yes I suppose so, maybe," she said absent-mindedly.

After a while, to my surprise, she continued, for the first time taking up the matter on her own initiative since we'd been together:

"I always thought I was a bad mother. I don't know why, perhaps that sort of feeling is forced on mothers, they're blamed for so much, or perhaps they have so much to fear and so much responsibility that they don't know how to bear it. But actually I've been a reasonably good mother. I never stinted on tenderness."

While we were talking, summer's first star rose in the eastern sky, the splendid Sirius. She stayed low above the sharp tops of the spruce trees, but within a short time moved from one side of the narrow window pane to the other and

185

vanished toward the south; she rose only to go down. Outside the veranda the ipomoea that had twined around the lilac bush opened two white flowers, and they seemed to glow so that all around them darkened—all signs of late summer. Mist rose from the lake, spreading gently toward the house along the grass, cloaking the shore and the water meadow and following the stream through the meadow as a low, winding cloud as far as the bridge and the roadside. The lights were already on in the farmhouse.

"I wonder how they're getting on there?" Tamara said.

did not succeed in ascertaining whether we were leaving or not, not to mention when and how.

As a result of Tamara's packing, there began to be bundles, bags, and packages in every corner, as if a crowd of vagabonds were lodging in the house. When she needed something she had to unpack many bags before she found what she was looking for. The unpacked things remained on the floor until I started to put them either on the shelves or in the cupboards or back in the bags. There was plenty to do, and in fact life seemed to have livened up considerably on account of Tamara's capriciousness. It was only to be regretted that, because of Kustaa Mauri's absence, we had drawn further away from each other. This could no longer be denied, however earnestly I might wish to reject awareness of it. It was new to me. Previously she had always taken refuge in me. I felt more clumsy than ever, and I too began to knock myself on the furniture and drop dishes from my hands, for I always seemed to have too many hands or too few. Tamara reproved me every time, called me clumsy dwarf, carcass, and mollusk. She started to beautify herself and was so successful that it made my heart ache. She cooled her burning body often by running into the lake at night, aggravating my insomnia. My brief periods of sleep were full of nightmares.

For a few days she ate only vegetables, made indeterminate salads from heaven knows what herbs, filled the yard with boxes and buckets to get pale dandelion leaves and plantains, which some nature healers recommended for restlessness. One day she managed to find blue clay and anointed herself all over with it. I was given the task of watching for the outside world while the clay dried and she lay on the narrow strip of sand on the shore, but looking at her the world was forgotten and I stared at the clay statue lying immobile before me, thinking that I had never seen anything so beautiful before and would certainly never see it again. I was supposed to patch over those places that she had not managed to do properly herself, and I smeared clay under her armpits, on her breasts that always moved just enough to break the clay, behind her ears, and finally I very carefully molded her features, stroking many times the curve of the lips, the nostrils, the lines in the forehead, and, as it were, penciling in the hairline straight and unbroken. Then I sat back to watch the clay dry. It shone dully at first like bronze with a patina, then it began to dry quite quickly and cracked as it dried. I patched it over again as long as there was enough clay. I kept covering the shoulders and hip bones, which tended to crumble first, and finally I completed my masonry— probably feeling for the only time in my life really perverse enjoyment—by placing the last lump as a seal between her legs, so that even her pubic hair was covered and she looked smooth and without apertures like a doll or the sexless statues of a hypocritical age. Here was a bride for me. Then— though at the same moment I felt I understood the whole divine devilry, as if I had consecrated myself to this joke—I drew a line on her with a dry reed stem so that she began to resemble a woman, a young, strapping, still hairless girl with that mysterious smile between her legs, on which nobody would dare to take an oath whether it would finally result in laughter or tears, a smile which many artists, once they have found it, have given to statues, idols, and paintings.

During those days I did not get any nearer to her than this.

I admired the way the clay dried, splitting into crisscross fissures, like the surface of an expensive pot, the molder's dream which is realized each time in a new and unexpected way, until I saw my idol stand up, crumble into a myriad pieces like Daniel's vision of the powers of the world, run to the water, and change into flesh and bone. When she had soaked the clay from herself she rose sparkling and as if newly created, and came beside me in the shade to dry herself.

"I'm in a bad temper," she said, twisting the towel in her ear.

I pretended surprise.

"Everything has become negative in me. My mind feels heavy. I'm tired. Putting up with unpleasant things takes all my strength away. It seems to me I'm blind and have lost all contact with myself. It's as if my eyes were turned inward and there was only darkness there. I see this landscape and I know it's in color, but I can't conceive it. What's happening to me?"

I was just about to open my mouth, but she was faster.

"Please don't say it's existential fear. A new idea would interest me for a moment, but you'll have to think of some definition that I've never heard."

So I kept my mouth shut.

Instead, I stroked her back; the skin did indeed feel even softer and smoother than before; it was a long time since she had let me do it. I tried to speak to her through touch, past the brain.

So our days went by, living on opposite banks of a misty river, waiting for the weather to clear.

One day Tamara asserted that the telephone wire had twisted itself back into its outlet.

"Was it disconnected?" I said, astounded.

"Yes. I disconnected it. I couldn't stand it lying in wait there all the time. Surely I have the right to be free during my vacation."

"Of course. One has to know how to get along without the gadget," I said, scrambling over to disconnect it again.

"Leave it alone," Tamara ordered. "Maybe someone wants to call about a really important matter. Would you look and see the receiver is properly in place—if it isn't one just gets a busy signal. And nothing is more humiliating than a properly connected phone that doesn't ring."

That night she could not get to sleep in spite of frequent swims and exhausting saunas. Nor did tea made from the leaves of lingonberries and wild raspberries, which we had picked ourselves, dried and carefully soaked, seem to help. At zero zero zero o'clock I recommended erotic literature, as she disturbed my light slumber with her twisting, turning, and moaning, especially when she was sleeping on her back. She did find among the old books a work entitled *A Young Woman's Pleasures and Duties* published at the turn of the century, modestly hidden behind the jacket of a detective novel, and started to examine it with great interest. After a while she threw the book away, ran outside, and the next moment a splash indicated that she required once more a cooling swim.

"Was it so exciting—I am sorry," I said to her when she came in shivering; the nights had begun to be cold.

"No, but the moral rules seem so sinful that I needed to rinse myself clean. Nothing beats Christian imagination for viciousness. No wonder priests have such a high potency— they lead the statistics you know. Think of a concept like the voluptuousness of sin. People like us will never know it."

After coming back from swimming she disconnected the

telephone again. It was as if by this act she could at least for a moment switch off the current of waiting, insignificant as it seemed, and small as all the other acts of these days were against the great absence of happening.

She was cold curled up in her bed on the floor, and I went over to warm her. I stooped down and breathed on her through the blanket. She straightened her legs, turned to let me in beside her, and she bent her arm to support my head while I pushed my left hand under her waist. We fitted in against each other; it was a long time since she had allowed me so near her, and we warmed each other.

So we spent the last night together on the floor, like passers-by in a strange house, all kinds of memories and associations surging through our dreams, becoming confused one with another in the freedom that lies beyond consciousness, and forming during the small hours many a vision and many a tongue, all of which we governed lightly thanks to the awareness, penetrating even through sleep, that we were sleeping there together.

In fact I slept badly, but I would not have exchanged this uncomfortable nearness for anything else. Several times I felt a desire to wake her and ask her without giving her time to control her response: "Do you love me?" I might even have said "Love me," commanded her unconscious energies, and who knows, perhaps in their surprise they would have obeyed, rushed with joy in my direction, to the permitted, wished-for channel, bring relief to us both.

She slept well, breathing on my forehead, and I felt a desire to stay awake to listen to the sound of her breathing.

In the early morning she drew away from me without waking, and I slept when the numbness in my limbs went away. When I awoke I had a rare feeling, which I suspect belongs to the world of family experience, and it is very possible that Tamara felt something similar too, for she said, looking at me with sleepy eyes from the bare floor, where at

191

some point in the early hours she had rolled from the mattress:

"I dreamed I'd been left an old spinster and I cried bitterly. And in my sleep I thought I woke up and there was a man sleeping beside me and on the other side a child and I myself was in the middle, married."

"Was it a good dream or a bad one?" I asked.

"A good one I suppose," she said, scrambling onto the mattress, stretching, warm and yawning beside me. "I kept congratulating myself that it was only a dream. Work that out if you can."

"You should try to avoid such complicated dreams; they are too difficult to interpret."

"It must have been because we were sleeping on the floor and side by side. But anyway I slept well. Do you have any objection if we leave tomorrow or the day after? Or even today."

"The journey will be awful as it has always been, so suit yourself. Just do not put any baskets of eggs in my lap."

"We must remember to go to the farm and say good-bye before we leave."

The scent of the barley field came right into the car as we drove past it. The stream had almost dried up, but from the wooded side beyond the bridge a brood of wild ducks burst into flight from it, scattering in all directions as if by an explosion. Along the roadside the brush had been sprayed with some poison and the landscape was dead before its time, surprised by a violent, malignant autumn, which had parched plants and turned young saplings brown.

"Terrible," Tamara said over and over again, "this is awful. When has this been allowed to happen?"

The taxi stopped in the farmyard so that we could say good-bye.

"It was the road repair committee that did it, though some of them were against it—they can see for themselves what it has done," said the farmer's wife.

"It may cause . . ." Tamara began, but then was silent. I guessed that she had intended to say that it might cause fetus damage, but this time she managed to stop in time. "It may cause the birds to die in the whole district and heaven knows what."

A round-faced, shy little boy was leaning against a ladder, playing with a bicycle pump; he must have been about six years old.

"This is our Pertti," the farmer's wife said. "Come and say how do you do, Pertti."

"No," said the boy, moving a safe distance away.

"He's with us for a trial period," said the young woman, lowering her voice. "Nobody wants to take them anymore at this age, they say. He's not really used to us yet. But we'll keep him all right, if we're allowed. He's got diabetes. We're going to take another child too so they'll be company for each other, if we can get one."

She went to fetch the eggs, which had been counted and packed.

"Good luck," Tamara said, tears in her eyes, "good luck, good luck."

She held her head very erect to stop the tears running down her cheeks, but when she began to pay for the eggs she no longer could and they streamed onto the money and her purse.

"Well, the money's blessed now," said the old farm woman, who had also joined us. "And may the eggs be too."

It turned out that I had to hold these blessed eggs in my lap after all during the first part of the journey. They had simply been dumped on my knees. What with the fuss of leaving and the surprise caused by the boy nobody had noticed my existence, which is always a relief for me. Or mostly: I might have been forgotten in some corner of the villa if I had not at the last minute drawn attention to myself. Only a cardboard cake box protected this fragile, easily breakable load entrusted to my care, symbolic of fruitfulness, happiness, and eternal life; with it in my hands I said good-

194

bye to this place, to summer, to my dreams and our days together.

Tamara cried at the beginning of the journey.

"The lease hasn't expired yet," she said at some point, "the heirs aren't going to start selling the house till autumn. We could still come back."

At that point, as I remember, I asked that the eggs be placed somewhere else. As was then done.

"But perhaps I may never see this place again," she said, bursting into tears once more, "not this place or these people, I'll never know what happens to them, we'll vanish from each other's sight like the woodpeckers in the forest."

"Don't worry. New sorrows will come."

On leaving we had looked for the last time into our mailbox. Tamara threw the local paper in my lap, not noticing the picture letter in its fold; the sunset glow had perhaps deepened a shade, the silhouettes darkened, and the lakeshore scenes yellowed like the sad-looking brush alongside our road; the boats had been pulled up on the rocks, and the farmer's wife was going to her barn chores and had stopped by the gate looking relieved that the summer visitors had left.

"Aren't you going to read your letter?" I asked after Tamara had, in my opinion, wept enough to exchange grief for the still waters of sadness.

"Letter? Who from? Why didn't you tell me?"

She blew her nose and I handed her Frans' resplendent missive. When she saw who the letter was from the brightened look on her face vanished and the hand she held out dropped down.

"You read it to me; I can't read in a car, I start feeling sick," she said, restraining herself bravely.

So I opened the letter and started to read it to her in the back seat of the taxi, with the twisting road throwing us against each other from time to time.

" 'Hello dear Friend. I greet you again from this bright hot

195

Helsinki and thank you for your letter which I was already waiting for, I was already wondering if my letter was not worth answering. I use your first name now Tamara, thank you, as I have done in my mind for a long time. I have not painted anything recently because I cannot concentrate in such hot weather and my mind always pines for the wrong track. I will try to rent a workroom in the autumn where I can live and paint in peace and also frame my pictures, as People often ask for the pictures I sell to be framed. I have framed some of them but in these circumstances it is difficult. Do you have your cripple friend there, I was not quite sure from your letter? If not then he misses you Tamara, I have noticed that he is a friend with a good memory and if he feels unhappy for a long time he will find it hard to forget his unhappiness.' "

"Now you're putting your own words in," Tamara said, sniffing.

"No I am not, look for yourself." I showed her the letter as she leaned against me at a turn in the road; on the right-hand side shone a lake which we were circling, the opposite shore covered with tents, summer cottages, cars, and trailers. "You yourself have always asserted that people care about one another."

" 'I measure this unhappiness according to the measure of my own self,' " I went on reading. " 'It seems to me that the upper end and the lower end should be looked after in harmony in turn. In my youth I have looked after my upper end with drink which has blunted me and the lower end has stayed' "—here the picture letter ended to continue on ordinary paper—" 'uncared for so that affects the nerves too and now both these things should be looked after so I do not become quite blunt as life is short anyway and my life has gone for nothing because of the fumes of booze. Now that I have left off drinking I would like sometimes now and then to look after my upper end and sometimes my lower end too

with you. I ask your pardon that I write straight confidentially. I do not want by any chance to offend the Human
Being in you Tamara, but I express myself by letting out my
feelings. I Value you above myself, and therefore reveal
myself confidentially to you and measure you by my own
yardstick and if you have understood me, you will grow by
my measure into a great Human Being with a noble soul, you
will be shining in my heart on my sick bed when I go with
my sins to Hell. Though I have a chance of going to Heaven
as I have not deceived any body, not you either Tamara. I
have suffered so much in life. God has disciplined me hard,
so I suppose he loves me also as the Book says. The social
structure has also done wrong to me. God has suffered this
to happen to me, so he surely loves me, so that I would
understand something and I have learnt something too as the
All Mighty has in my suffering opened my thoughts a little.
Greetings, farewell I say with burning lips. Frans Siltanen.
Confidential Councillor. Inspector of Landscapes. Some time
I will write a bit more for you to think about.' "

"Nothing missing except that it should have been from
Kustaa Mauri," I said, handing the letter to Tamara.

"Don't! I can't stand hearing even his name. And now I'll
have to hurt Frans's feelings. I'll have to tell him that you
are pathologically jealous, that you'd strangle me if you knew
I had other affairs. Otherwise he'll try again."

"The portrait of my character is beginning to become quite
colorful."

"I feel that cares and sorrows are waiting for us with open
arms," Tamara said, "all the sorrows of those who imagine
they can and will get help from others. Some people, when
they look in the mirror, see worms coming out of their eyes.
I see a big tunnel in front of us, legs apart like a huge bowel,
and we'll be forced to swim in it against the current until
we're vomited out somewhere or other. That's how I see our
return to urban life. I'm like people's very own intestinal

197

parasite that they feed and sometimes even imagine they love. You on the other hand are one of those surface parasites, a flea, a louse, a tick, you just bite into the body of society and fulfill your task in this terrifying, stinking, rotting phenomenon called life. Why couldn't life have been healthier, pleasanter? Because it happened to be born in stagnant water. Those with an acute sense of smell started to scramble onto land. But rotting follows them everywhere. Life is the blink of an eye before rotting. The moment when you dream of being saved. I can understand why people want to be embalmed or cremated. I want to throw up."

"Should we stop?" asked the driver. "The lady doesn't seem too well."

"Just drive on," mumbled Tamara.

"Sorry, but I need some fresh air myself, feel funny for some reason," the driver said, pulling over to the side of the road and rapidly walking away.

"I feel just like he does," Tamara commented. "I'd like to break off this journey, I don't want to arrive nor to stay in this car. I don't belong where I'm going, but I don't belong back there either, by the shore and in a strange house. Nobody misses me, and I don't miss anyone."

"There are plenty of people who miss you," I said. They are all waiting there to tell you their troubles; even Frans needs someone who'll listen."

"You sound horribly therapeutic," she said. "It's all just despair. A desperate person catches at anything. It's like a cramp, the first and last human reaction, besides the cry, of course."

"Well, a cramp is better than nothing."

"I'm going to start working for something simple, concrete. Homes for these people. Jobs. I can't go on helping their souls, consoling them. Where can I always find the consolation? This is my hopelessness. I don't want to live without love and significance. I'll have to choose some simple, clear road, always keep repeating it, have it written in front of me, on every paper that I read, as Luther wrote: 'This is my flesh and this is my blood.' When you said there's a letter here, like a fool of course I thought, it's from Kustaa Mauri."

I had only vaguely understood the connection between her last sentence and everything that had flooded out before. I only realized that disappointment acted once again as a lever which with one jerk upset her balance, made her lose her faith in people and relations between people, and the things that she valued and trusted most: her work, her methods, her sincerity. I'm sure that I'm not exaggerating; I believe that even the smallest motions of love can release enormous power, both constructive and destructive. Love is truly creative. But it is capricious, never at anybody's command, as hard to tame as a bird or words. It comes only on its own terms, which it mercilessly dictates.

I do not know what I said to Tamara as we sat in the car parked by the roadside while the driver smoked a cigarette a little way off, looking at the lake. I remember her smiling and sometimes agreeing. It was a surprise for both of us to see the turn our journey had taken.

"Does the lady feel better?" the driver said, starting the car again."You see, I'm very sensitive. In this job you ought to be used to everything, but there are things that revolt me. The smell and talk of drunks, I'm used to that. It took years, but after all I've got a family. Then I've got a rubber truncheon here under the seat in case someone gets violent. I've never used it, but nowadays you have to be prepared for anything. But in the daytime and from sober people, especially just after a meal, I can't bear hearing just anything. There are three things I hate—a hair in my soup, worms in meat, and everything rotten. I can't bear to see them, I don't want them on my plate, and I can't stand hearing about them, especially not in my own car."

"Well, there's not much left for you to enjoy," I said,

trying to be funny. "But you are quite right. The mutiny on the *Potemkin* started because there were worms in the meat and we all know the consequences of that."

"Well, it's certainly not every day I have customers like you. There are people that talk about art and culture. Only yesterday I had a professor of technology I had to drive to Helsinki because his wife had the car. He talked all the way about how technology makes people happy, frees them for creative work and many interests, folk music for instance. I play my own compositions on the accordion and I'm certainly as good as many another; it's just I don't have a name and if you're unknown . . . You can play alone all right, why not, it gives satisfaction, but it's really something when there's listeners and you get appreciation, applause, slaps on the shoulder, and a bit of praise. It's like you've got more right to play when you give pleasure to more people. We really agreed on a lot of things, me and the professor—those professors know about things all right. That's just how I've seen things since I put my fields in the soil bank. See this car? I play it like a musical instrument. And my accordion I finger like a woman. All the time when I'm playing I listen to what the instrument wants to give itself. And when I'm driving it's nice to look at the scenery and listen to nice cultured talk. I've had my fill of injustice and abuse, but the grumblings of a guy like me won't change things. Sometimes it seems to me that the guilty ones are sitting right there in the back of the car. Though nowadays there are plenty of good places where you can get your nerves cured."

"Well, to tell the truth that's the sort of place we're on the way to," I said boldly.

"Oh, that explains things," the driver said understandingly. "Cigarette?"

Tamara was coldly silent, but as the journey went on the driver and I exchanged reminiscences, childhood memories, and opinions, spicing our talk with a few exaggerations that are necessary to establish a quick contact with a stranger. We also disagreed courteously and pulled each other's leg so that by the end of the trip we had learned to respect each other sufficiently to part friends. Finally the driver praised Tamara as if she were a horse temporarily in poor shape.

"Don't worry, it'll be all right," he said. "It's no good expecting too much from women. A good-looking girl she is, if only she'd stop sulking. Here you are, ma'am, safely home and no eggs broken."

So we arrived at my place over piles of newspapers, amid the dust; the peculiar smell of home is always noticeable after an absence. Mine smelled of books, stagnant air, and the instruments I have to use. In addition there seemed to float here the scent of my thoughts, a mild distant aroma that was perhaps more characteristic of my home than anything else.

"I'll put everything in order for you here," Tamara said. "And we'll eat together. But then I'll go over to my place. I must be alone, need to be alone. I'm so upset that I need calm and solitude to begin to see again."

"Don't bother with housekeeping," I told Tamara. "I have plenty of time."

More than anything else I feared that she would begin to fuss around, move hurriedly and bang about around me. That sort of thing always made me feel that something terrible was happening and I would get trampled on.

"Please," I said.

"All right, I'll rest here for a minute," she said and lay down on the bed, my own wide bed.

I lay down beside her and felt that now I might relax, like a hunter's dog that rests only when his master is snoring and his shotgun is hung up.

"You are my rest," I said. "You are my home." Those words belonged to this room.

"I'm not at home anywhere," Tamara said. "I'm lost now and afraid of searchers, I'm tired, how can I manage even to go to work. And when I think how different it could have been, how strong I would have felt. . . . I hate him because of this lack of strength."

"Supposing he expects you to do something, he is used to you taking the initiative."

"No! I've already humbled myself too much. He won't know how I've suffered, that pleasure he won't get. He knows it's up to him to make the first move."

I felt how her diaphragm tensed while she was speaking about Kustaa Mauri, her whole body was rigid, it carried disappointment like a foreign body that hardened at every word. That's what tired her. Love, your name is pain.

"But what a stupid thing for me to hope for the impossible," Tamara went on, as if she wanted to empty herself of all her distress here, so that nothing would remain to take home. "I wanted to believe the unbelievable."

"H'm," I said, surprised by this conclusion, "I don't know if I'd go as far as to say that."

"Funny," she said. "I couldn't stand him without love, you I can stand. There are people one just couldn't put up with at all. Kustaa Mauri is one of them."

If I had imagined I understood the situation in some way, after these explanations that delusion vanished completely. Everything seemed to me more confused than ever before during the whole business. The only things that seemed clear were: Kustaa Mauri had showed no sign of life and Tamara missed him bitterly. Tamara had been the active party in the relationship, but could not get in touch with the man. Kustaa Mauri, who had achieved virility only through Tamara, did not wish for some reason to eat the whole cake, which Tamara had clearly imagined would last inexhaustibly for the rest of her life. And I, who was supposed to live on the crumbs of their plenty and the fruits of my own spirit and who had rejoiced over all this in advance, was going to be left empty-handed. The worst thing was that for a long time she had not fed my imagination in any way; I'd had to invent everything myself, the equivalent of which is mastur-

202

bation. But worse still was that she cheated me. When one day I ventured to complain to her about my fate in this triangle she quite coldly started to plagiarize worn-out subjects from literature, stories about monks and experienced, skillful abbesses, the early fathers of the church, and frightened novices. She even resorted to themes from third-rate films, gorillas and Christian maidens or the cannibal and the white woman. The level of her choice hurt me so much that I reminded her in her own words: "I too wanted sincere, simple, shared experiences that the licentiousness of monks could not give me."

At least I stopped the flow of lewd tales with which men tried to stave off boredom over the centuries. But our life did not become happier. It seemed that we had reached a dead end, why deny it.

heard nothing from her for a long time until she phoned me from work. She did not have much time to talk.

"Mirja's come back. And the dancing boy, remember?"

"Yes, I do."

"She talks about you. It seems to me that she wants to meet you. What do you say?"

"No, not now. Maybe later."

I knew how their return must pain Tamara. She had often told me that she sent her patients out into the so-called normal world only to see them return a few months later.

"How are you yourself?"

"Fine, fine after such a good holiday," she said gaily.

"Any news from Kustaa Mauri?" I risked.

"No—why? Are you still thinking about him?"

"You haven't been around lately. What do you do in the evenings?"

"Have a good time."

"What about your need for continuity?"

"I've been having a continuous good time. By the way, that boy who danced himself well. Do you know why he danced so well and freely with me then, with such conviction? He told me about it. It was because some girl he was in love with was sitting and watching. He danced for that girl. That's why the dance was successful and significant. And that was why he never managed to dance so well again afterward. Not even with me. He said he became conscious of it only later. He's aggressive and withdrawn again. He has no money, no job, no place to go, nobody wants him because of his illness. In fact, he's dangerous in his present state. But he's got his life before him and he'll have a better phase again, but where will he go then? They'll certainly make him an outpatient pretty soon."

"There would not have been problems like this if you had studied the psychology of language."

It was my old refrain and she started laughing. I felt better immediately; oh, how I enjoyed that burst of laughter.

"Do you know how it affected me coming back here?" she said, a shade more lightly (or perhaps I only imagined it). "Many of the nurses and other staff often say that they're surprised when they come back from vacation that the people here are just the same as those they've met during their holidays. I, on the other hand, feel that we all ought to be here. Why are you and Kustaa Mauri running around loose?"

"Really, what can one say to that! There is undeniably something attractive about the idea."

"But of course you're too rich to be here," she said, and now I understand what I had taken for detachment was in fact defiance and that she wanted to hurt me in the absence of anyone better. "Only poor people come here. The rich have their own places, they go abroad or are looked after at home. The only people who come here are those who have nothing to lose but their job and their self-respect. After they leave, they find only closed doors. Everybody is afraid of these people. They're considered dangerous. And yet they themselves are afraid of everything. Fear and insecurity are the things that make a man aggressive. He feels he's threatened and defends himself as if he's fighting for his life at every moment, even when it's not necessary."

I was used to such outbursts, it was the same after every holiday. She rebelled against everything that she was compelled to resign herself to accept. She still needed me for relief.

"I will try to talk again to that politician I know. Though it nauseates me to plead with these people, especially in vain."

She started to thank me effusively, as she had when I had telephoned my friend the first time. At least she still seemed to cling to the childish belief that matters are arranged by a few telephone calls.

"I'll come and see you one of these evenings, or one night, if you'd like it. I've got my key. I've got one or two things to tell you but nothing especially exciting. You always need emotion and sensation."

Suddenly I felt bad, and I all but said: Have you been unfaithful to Kustaa Mauri? While I was pondering, she said a quick good-bye. I only had time to promise to telephone my reluctant councillor again.

Afterward I sat for a long while in the same place, wondering what had touched me so deeply. I no longer had much tendency toward jealousy; that had diminished at the same rate as the sensations in my lower extremities. If I remember rightly, it comes back only on special occasions, like the Kustaa Mauri affair. Now I was clearly suffering from the idea that Tamara had been having "a good time" with someone else.

A person can be forgiven for everything except his absence. The thought is not originally mine but Aldous Huxley's. He could hardly have been the first to think of it; nor I the last.

N ow it was my turn to hear footsteps and imagine I saw
Tamara approaching at the street corner, endlessly
coming nearer under the aspens, turning to cross the
road to enter the yard through the squeaking side gate. Many
times I raised my hand in greeting and was about to call from
the window to hear her answer as soon as she was in hearing
distance. I could hardly wait for her to run up the steps and
before that perhaps stop to complain about the abundance
of weeds in the flower beds, the untended and unwatered
slope where sorrel and red-tipped young aspen were poking
through. But as if by evil magic she always changed into a
stranger just when I was finally about to see her face. Suddenly an unknown woman stood at the gate looking for quite
another address, and the dark-haired being to whom I had
smiled and waved walked by with closed face: the familiar
way of walking that I had imagined was hastening toward
me changed before my eyes to mocking bustle, and the skirt
that I thought I recognized from afar went past swinging

scornfully. I hobbled from room to room pressing in moist hands things she had brought or she owned, little drop-shaped bottles of hair-setting lotion, a deodorant, bits of clothing she had forgotten or had intentionally left at my place, little panties that must be tight as a girdle over her hips, and discarded pantyhose which had been left for use when she was cleaning (as if she had ever done any cleaning at my place) or could be worn with slacks in the country (she had forgotten to take them). I pushed my hand into them, stretched them on my fingertips; they were incredibly thin and elastic. Some of them glowed a little and reminded me of her legs. In some of her clothes there were still re-minders of her shape and odors. A pillow smelled of her hair, the upper part of a nightgown that she seldom used smelled familiarly of her skin and of some very mild perfume, maybe from soap or a skin cleanser or the suntan oil she had used during the holiday. The lower part reminded me of my mother and—this may be pure imagination—of mother's milk. I've always noticed the same odor in mother's milk and other female secretions. No doubt that's why men like to take a woman with their mouth, lick her all over, something which Tamara always wonders at.

If I had been told that it was cruel of her to leave me in this way in uncertainty and waiting, I would have denied it, but actually I knew she was neglecting me unscrupulously after our holiday together, was unjustly causing me the same pain that Kustaa Mauri had caused her. After all, it may have been an earned punishment, just by a morality unknown to me according to which I deserved this suffering, the only kind that could still really hurt me. I was unable to work and knew I was not fit for anything until my relationship with Tamara was stabilized again. I suffered more than ever from my infirmity. I hated my feeble limbs, and it seemed to me they emitted a bad smell. I had a remote relation who lay in bed for forty years with his legs totally paralyzed—thus more helpless even than I—until his lower body rotted away, after which he finally could die. He read a lot, he had a splendid sense of humor and not an ounce of self-pity; he was intelligent and could be healthily malicious. I have collected material about him and perhaps will write it up one day. He had also been in love; the affair had lasted several years though I assume it was platonic. The beloved had later got married, after having brought her fiancé to her friend for approval. And he had given them his blessing. For a while they had all three seen each other often, like friends, until the idyll died its natural death. This only happened to come to my mind because of my agitation and the fact that my thoughts wandered, seeking comfort even from the experiences of bygone generations.

Other signs of an exceptional state of mind appeared. Tamara had once brought me sex manuals and similar literature giving precise information about how many minutes sexual intercourse should last, how many movements were needed to achieve an orgasm, and what should be done if it was not achieved. The shape of the bed seemed of paramount importance and the intensity of sensations could be measured by the redness of the body and the location of drops of sweat. We had spent a whole evening on these books. The members of Tamara's sex club constantly referred to them and wanted her opinion on one question or another. Therefore she had to study them and thought that perhaps they would amuse me as the tales of *The Thousand and One Nights* had amused the Caliph Sheherban. We were both tired after we had waded through the books. I recall that my attention was mostly on the lovers' legs, which were twisted into positions each stranger than the last, and would remain eternally unattainable for me, and much less on their bodies, which were wound around each other like question marks. I thought how bored with each other they must be to bother to do all that; it seems as if they're just trying not to see each other, Tamara had said, or else they're doing it as a substitute for gymnastics.

I now turned the pages of these books sadly, hoping they would give me a little sexual aggression that would cheer me up, but it was a vain hope. I only began to see Tamara in all those peculiar positions, which did not excite me in the least. Then the doorbell rang. I broke my hobbling record as I dragged myself to open it.

At the door stood Frans, neat and tidy as ever, wearing a checked summer shirt and carrying the bag in which his tools were.

"Anything to sharpen?" said Frans, a smile of reunion on his face, baked the shade of red cabbage.

I started to wish him welcome but before I had managed it he had stepped inside and was already looking at the books.

"I see you are interested in all sort of things," he said in a voice trembling with admiration.

I hastened to assure him that this was a small, quite unimportant sideline compared with my real interests; one must for professional reasons try to keep up with all aspects of literature.

"Is that it—that's what I've thought," said Frans ambiguously, examining the picture in which a man and a woman sat glued to one another like chairs piled on one another after a ball. "I understand all right. This is like getting to peep into someone's bedroom, though I'm not sure how much pleasure you get from it. It reminds me of a poor starving fellow who either reads a cookbook or watches others stuff themselves."

"True, true," I muttered in my chagrin, gathering up the books and cursing the fact that Frans had managed to surprise me like this; it was not that I wished to hide anything, but I would have liked to prepare an introduction, to make it clear that this was not a case of voyeurism or pornography. . . . But explanation was not necessary.

"Never mind," Frans nodded understandingly, "just let 'em stay where they are. I see you've been alone."

It seemed quite unnatural to admit my loneliness to him

with the nude pictures in my lap, so I answered in as offhand and convincing a voice as I could command:

"I have an extensive and lively circle of friends; they barely let me work during the day, but in the evenings they just flood in."

"Ah," said Frans, "and I'm one of those that can get along on my own. I haven't got any relatives, and in flophouses you don't really make friends. Everybody there just hopes to get away, everybody thinks it's temporary even if it lasts ten years. They're the people that know what loneliness is even if there's only three feet between the beds and the breath smells everywhere you turn your nose."

Thus he got to boasting in my own special area, solitude, and on top of that asked: "Where's the missus, I mean Miss Tamara? I haven't managed to meet her, not in the evenings nor the daytime, so I thought maybe she's here. I've got the idea that you have a very close spiritual relationship."

I now had to confess that I had not seen Tamara since we had come back from the country, and that I did not know when I would. And when at last Frans sat down by the kitchen table and took his tools for sharpening out of his bag and I started to make tea for the two of us, I found myself confessing that I missed her very much, had been missing her all these days; that's why I had dug out the cursed books, but they had not managed to stimulate me in the least.

"Me too," Frans admitted humbly, "I've been counting the days till I meet Tamara. Every morning when I wake up at Peace Haven Four on my bunk I think that today I'll see her for sure, but by evening I still haven't, either at home or near her work." Frans told me he had walked around there many days, only he had not had the nerve to get too close in case someone pulled him in for a cure and all he wanted was his freedom and Tamara.

There we were, two unfortunates confessing our love for the same woman, boasting of our sadness and longing, declaring in unison how highly we valued noble sentiments,

211

both those which united us in friendship and those which we felt for Tamara.

"I'm making some tea for us," I said in an earnest voice.

"I'd rather have coffee," said Frans, emboldened by our mutual misfortune.

I put the coffee on, while the number of ground and glittering steel weapons on the table grew. There were plenty of things to be sharpened: garden shears, kitchen scissors, nail scissors, ordinary scissors, and no longer usable scissors. Frans even discovered the cheese slicer could be sharpened.

"Do you have any boiled potatoes, sir, or could you let me boil a few potatoes, 'cause we're not allowed to cook there."

And while he went on grinding and grinding I cleaned potatoes and put them on, and imagined a future in which Tamara and Frans sat at the table and I was their humble and diligent servant, whom they ordered about in turn. That reminded me that Frans and I had got on first-name terms ages ago, and I reminded him of it.

"Why did you start sirring me?" I asked.

"I don't know, I was just thinking about her, I suppose."

"And I was so mixed up, I thought it was her that was ringing and then you came and caught me looking at these pictures."

"Things like that happen, people's fates get twisted up in a funny way," said Frans, finally completing his work. He wrapped his file in gray flannel and began to drink coffee. The potatoes started to boil.

"You know the truth of it is," Frans said, swallowing, "a man always wants drink or women. Funny but when I was young I preferred drink—it's only lately I've started fancying women. Probably because I gave up drink. And I really liked it, I mean alcohol, and I still like it, but when the doctor gave me two choices—the grave or milk—I chose milk and life, and I never guessed that sufferings like this were still awaiting me. Stuff like wine I've never gone in for, that's the speed of the French; queer people, they torture and kill geese to gobble their livers."

Frans spoke like a man who at least knew his limits and weaknesses. He made me think of phrases like "neat, clean, and sober as a former alcoholic," only I didn't know where or how to use them. He read a lot and intensively, which was reflected in his speech, and preferably such books as "set you thinking," as he said. He was one of those rare Finnish citizens who had read *Seven Brothers* many times and voluntarily. Once when he came I had a history of literature open on my desk. He glanced at it and immediately commented on one of our nineteenth-century writers.

In addition to paying him for his work, I often gave him some books, on which he pronounced his judgment on his following visit. He valued books that were "psychologically right" and that remained to "vex the mind" and described the "reality of life." I gave him some books this time too, as a mark of our deepened friendship, and urged him to pass them on to someone else if he did not care for them himself.

"I won't give these to just anyone," he said, pushing the books into his bag. "I'll only give them to those who will be grateful."

At the door he asked if I couldn't spare any of "those books," maybe some of the smaller ones that would easily go in the pocket and would not be too conspicuous. And so he tenderly placed *The ABC of Love* in his bag alongside some hot potatoes wrapped in newspaper.

"Don't you feel like going out on such a nice evening?" he said as he was leaving. "I couldn't stay in one place in weather like this, not that it depends on the weather, I have to be on the move rain or shine, shiver or sweat."

And so I came to tell Frans something that I had not even told Tamara: that I would like to sit in a park and watch children at play; children always interested me, I often compare a child's feelings with my own longing for nearness.

213

At some stage their helplessness is even greater than mine and they are at the mercy of adults to a greater extent than I. But society only accepts the young, healthy, and productive. Everything else is superfluous; only love transgresses this rule sometimes. I told Frans how I had had to give up even this pleasure; I had been in the habit of going to sit on a bench by a playground and observe the children's behavior for hours; I felt sad every time I saw how even kindness was used to suppress a child's will and creativity and was delighted whenever one of them broke loose from the square of the sand pit. At one time I sat there every day. Then the mothers and guards began to take notice of me and one day a policeman came and spoke to me. This is one of the most depressing memories of my life and I can't talk about it further. In shops, supermarkets, and discount stores I have been treated with suspicion too because people always doubt whether I have any money. That seems to be the biggest crime in our world. But I do not wish to dwell on that too long either; I cannot afford to be bitter.

I felt ashamed after this outburst in front of Frans and wished that he would leave quickly. I had exposed secrets I had not intended to expose to anyone. I had never, never wanted to say aloud the words that had now been spoken.

Frans had nodded while I was speaking and made grunting sounds as a sign of understanding. But now it seemed that I had told him such a common tale that it was not worthy of comment.

He said: "That's how it is."

Then he picked up his bag, bulging with books, and we said a cordial good-bye.

After the door had shut I felt so faint that I had to grab the doorpost so as not to fall. I felt pain as I had not felt it for a very long time and hoped I would never need to see Frans again, so that his presence would not remind me of my miserable indiscretion.

E very night I rescued her from drowning and never knew whether I succeeded or not. Sometimes I got her to the surface, but when I tried to breathe air into her lungs, her mouth was full of mud, and when I pushed my finger between her teeth to clean the ooze away, she slipped from my hands back into the darkness. "Help," I shouted in my empty house, "Help," so that I woke up, to slip back in a moment into sleep, as a woman in labor is said to sleep between each spasm. Sometimes she had held on to a water-lily stem with her teeth like a dying mallard, and I raised her with the flower in her mouth, dragged her by the hair—she was light in the water, but the current swept her away and I was almost choked myself. Sometimes I got her as far as the shore; a little leech had sucked itself into her ear tip like a glittering jewel, her breasts were covered with mollusks, an eel flapped between her legs. And many times in the night I took her head between my hands, her mouth to my mouth, and tried to blow life into her, life that I scarcely had in myself. And when I tried to drag her onto the land so that when she revived she would not try to get back in the water, she had partly turned into a sunken log that lay with its end deep in the mud, had lain there for a long time, water-logged, become heavy and undecaying as sometimes happens, and the part that I was dragging began to disintegrate in my hands and I was filled with greater anguish than ever. I began to gather up the pieces, to fit them together to see what was really left, but they disintegrated as I touched them, and fish darted to the surface to eat them, terns began to circle above with quarrelsome cries, and flies appeared in spite of night and the wind, which made the leaves and dark river dance. And I knew that only he who has searched for his loved one in the river of death knows what love is. I no longer cared about the future, it was a black indifferent stream that swept coldly past such as I. It was the past I was fishing for here, our past, my right to what had been and through it to the present. And that by decaying in my hands, by denying her existence to me, she took from me this primordial dimension. But I did not intend to surrender her, whatever shape she took to escape me; if she disintegrated into plankton I would be a whale to receive her. Suddenly the stream became burning hot, it was the stream of my sweat, my collected, canalized pains, my spiritual erection, my exalted ejaculation, and my stock of unspilt sperm; she would drown in that. We would be united for eternity and expanded into a quiet pool, and nobody who saw its shimmering bright bed many fathoms deep would think that it could be otherwise.

In the daytime I pushed her out of my mind by working. "The identity of the intelligentsia is today in every way a questionable and dubious matter. Its integrity must be examined. Accusations should be leveled against intellectuals. They have disappointed the expectations of their parents. When working-class parents who have had little education send their children to school, they do it in the hope that the children will become gentlemen, academically accomplished and furnished with degrees, civil servants, teachers, doctors, clergymen, engineers. What they really want for their children is a better life than they had, a higher income, a more respected position, and a more gentlemanly way of life."

Every now and then I listened for the telephone but it did not ring. And even if the telephone had rung, it would probably have been for Tamara. Her answering service had assured me for days that she was at my place. Where, I asked it, whereabouts have I hidden her? Hearing my own number repeated so often made me think that there was some secret code; perhaps people were changing into numbers, escaping from existence to wavelengths, frequencies, and cassettes, from which, after a suitable period of nonexistence, they would be discharged as people again, when the memories and unnecessary emotional fixations were eliminated from them.

My thoughts tended to wander, but I compelled them back to work. "The intelligentsia can be accused," I wrote, "the intelligentsia can be accused. . . ." What the deuce could these scallywags be accused of now? Yes, quite: The intelligentsia can be accused of appropriating the achievements of the working class to themselves. "Now that the working class has succeeded in creating for itself an identity arousing respect, organized itself in a trades-union movement with a strong sense of self-awareness and a real significance in the economic, political, and social life of the country, these intellectuals with their feeble self-awareness, driven by a crisis of identity, come and say: 'We too are laborers.' "

That's the stuff!

The letter box clattered and something fell on the floor lightly like a letter. Would I be informed at least that she had been found somewhere? Or would I first read about her in the newspaper, finally see her date of birth and the names of a countless number of deeply sorrowing relations, who always, as if by a miracle, proliferate in obituaries. This fantasy sent me hobbling to the door. With the sharp spike

217

on my stick (which I had designed myself) I hooked up from beneath the letter box a piece of paper promising to tell me what every house owner should know if he wished to be considered a decent citizen.

I would probably decide to live some years after Tamara— if she was really dead—from sheer curiosity. It would be damned interesting to see what would happen to my body and soul, what more could be devised, what variations the landscape of negativity would offer in the course of time. Maybe I'd rot away like my distant relative. It would be interesting to know what happens in the brain while the body is decaying. There is only one difficulty. I cannot stand pain or bad smells. Pain I would not feel, at any rate in the initial stages, assuming that the putrefaction would begin from the toes, but the smell might be a stumbling block; even the odor of sweaty feet is sometimes unbearable when I meet normal walking beings.

Then a thought struck me—surprising that I did not think of it before. I would leave my body to the university's Department of Anatomy. My only condition would be that my erectile center be examined with particular care, its organic connections with the spinal cord, the pituitary gland, and testicles be thoroughly investigated, also its dependence on the regulation on the one hand of the hormones, on the other hand of the cerebrum, in as far as this might still be possible in a lifeless body—but after all Galvani managed to make frog legs jerk, and think what followed from that! And that these results be compared with purely psychological studies accumulating all over the world, and that the whole be studied in the light of emotional life as a whole. Some young enthusiastic, talented scientist could lead the decisive study—only devotion and money would be needed. My will would provide the incentive for all sorts of activities. A door-to-door campaign: "Support Those Who Cannot Stand Erect." Creative forces would be assembled. Thinkers and doers would be dug out from the rank and file of the nation.

The establishment of an idea bank would be essential right from the start. Personal keep-fit programs would be available at health centers. Erotic literature would burst into unprecedented abundance. People would enjoy themselves, there would be a new affirmation of life. The prospects would be illimitable.

My fingers trembling with joy and inspiration, I pulled out the sheet in my typewriter and started to compose a letter to the Department of Anatomy. I felt that this was the crowning deed of my life. I was a benefactor of mankind. There is no more genuine feeling than that when a man is moved by his own nobility. Tears coursed down my cheeks, I wept for the first time for ages. Something had matured inside me, and I began to be quits with life. Now at last I was free. I no longer belonged even to myself.

I furnished the letter with my signature, my academic degree, and address. It was impressive. The general appearance was good too, I had succeeded in typing the whole letter without a single mistake, a rare event for me. I admired it for a moment, the most important literary achievement of my life, placed it in its envelope, sealed it, and put a stamp on it. Everything was ready. I felt that I had attended to myself right to the end, fulfilled my last duty toward this wretched monster called the body—not that it did not have certain amusing features. I was now finally on the winning side, a former human being.

Intoxicated with joy, I moved from one room to another without realizing at all how awkward it was for me. I felt so cheered that I decided to telephone to Tamara's place of work and ask for her there, although I knew that she did not like it. I was told that she had not been at work at all the last few days; she was probably taking the remainder of her holiday or might be ill; it would be best to inquire again when the ward sister was there. Depression spread through me as if the paralysis had started to move up from the areas it had already occupied. I stared at the letter on the desk wondering where its magic power had suddenly gone, and it was as if I saw Tamara's head rising and falling with the waves amid the glitter out on the lake. No new idea could save me.

I forced myself to continue my work and felt that I hated the intellectuals more than ever. Suddenly I thought I saw Frans sitting in the basket chair beside my desk, tidy and sober, with his worn bag beside him, the desire for drink and women his only companion. And next to him the great intelligentsia like a many-headed monster sitting around and talking in expensive restaurants, blind drunk.

I was in a state similar to temporary insanity induced by strain, sleeplessness, and nightmare. Exhausted, I finally admitted to myself that the only value of the piece was that by stimulating me, by leading me into uncertain areas that I did not master, as I mastered the emotional life, it kept Tamara out of my mind. This was my way of admitting that I could not stand waiting and uncertainty either. At some late hour I drank a little wine and took a sleeping pill; by means of this forbidden combination I hoped I could finally sleep. I do not know whether several hours had passed or several days and nights when I heard her come.

She was a living reincarnation of the drowned creature whom I had fished out night after night from the muddy waters of my dream lake. Her hair was damp and unkempt, her features immobile, her lips lax and swollen. She dropped into the chair by my desk, the one where I had imagined Frans sitting, and closed her eyes. A half-moon shone through a window on the eastern side. Venus was on her way down in a cold-looking glowing sky. The grass in the garden was gray with dew. I concluded that it must be close to dawn.

"Tamara," I said, grasping her hands, which were cold as ice. "Where have you been?"

She did not answer or even seem to have heard, just sat there with closed eyes.

I would have liked to do as in the dream, to take her head between my hands, her mouth to my mouth, to breathe life into her, hold her so tightly that she could not suddenly vanish again, bind her by her hair to my fingers so that she could not get away from me again, and for that very reason hardly dared to stir. I began to rub her hands cautiously, remembering how familiar this gesture was, and pressed her

221

ice-cold white fingertips against my lips, breathed on them. Gradually they began to warm up and I ventured to speak. I said softly that I had missed her and waited for her, had suffered terribly, did not deserve such treatment. Each word brought me relief, like loosening a tight shirt button by button.

And suddenly she opened her eyes and said, pain permanently lodged in her gaze like a nocturnal animal:

"I told you and you did not believe me. Now you know. Only it's useless knowledge."

"I know," I said, kissing her wrists, warming the spots where the artery was near the skin. "I admit it."

"Don't humble yourself too much, you'll feel worse later."

"I am not humbling myself."

I had got down on my knees beside her and put my arm around her, laid my head in her lap and breathed her in, buried my face in her, rubbed my chin and ears against her breasts, pushed my nose under her arms, kissed her neck; her hair smelled of night and, as I touched it, seemed to rustle like reeds.

"I was so afraid for you. Where have you been?"

"If you really must know, I've been with the underpants man."

"That communist?"

"Right."

"Why him of all people?"

I began to feel that my trials were not yet over. I felt dizzy. Suddenly I understood those who squeeze the neck of their beloved until the thumbs press the windpipe right against the spine; so I had to endure this identification too.

"Well, who would you have recommended?" Tamara said.

I could not get up from the floor, but I did not wish to remain there either. I wriggled far enough away to be able to lean against the bookshelf.

"What is there to upset you in that?" she said. "After all this isn't the first time. Or is it those long underpants you

222

detest so much? As a matter of fact I missed them, it would have been so cozy and domestic to see him pattering about in them. But he was wearing the briefest of bikini shorts and bulged as handsomely as they do in the ads."

"Undressed and ready, as usual," I said, with my eyes closed in turn.

"No, not this time, though actually I wished he was. But he has a very funny style. He never makes advances or suggests going to bed. He just gets undressed and goes there himself without saying a word. It's up to me then whether I go after him or not. Generally I do."

I normally never asked Tamara to do anything for me, but now I said: "Would you get me a glass of water?"

For some reason it sounded solemn and fateful, as if I had asked for extreme unction, as if Tantalus had finally admitted his thirst. And perhaps for that reason she did as I asked. I drank slowly, and the glass, the water, and swallowing seemed strange, as if my mouth had been numb.

"How did you run into him?" I asked after I had finished drinking. For some reason I had great difficulty in speaking, but I could not remain silent.

"I phoned him. I said it would be nice to meet."

It took so long before I could form the following sentence that I feared I had been stricken by aphasia. I realized that I had never taken this kind of paralysis into account in my scheme for the future. It may be of course that this pause seemed long only to me, who experienced the inner effort contained in it.

"How did you . . . ? You didn't surely . . . How could you now in this case . . . ?"

"I understand what you're trying to say. The answer is quite simple. He doesn't mean anything to me. I don't mean anything to him. There's no question of submitting or humbling. I wouldn't even be hurt if he'd said he didn't have time. But he did. Plenty even. I think he was almost glad, even though he's always just as sour-looking behind that beard. And we play well together. He's well equipped, as they say. A piece of meat that's always standing so it's a constant nuisance. D'you understand, my dear dead balls?"

"Why such language?" I stuttered.

"I'm developing. This is my psycho-linguistic evolution. You should appreciate it."

Suddenly I felt a desire to be insulting and began:

"One of those men for whom any woman will do . . ."

"Far from it," Tamara interrupted. "I'm the only one he's accepted who's not a member of the Party. He's told me himself he doesn't go to bed with anyone unless they have a Party card."

"Just a minute," I said, "I believe I recognize the old ram. He's one of those nauseating intellectuals."

"Oh, there are dozens of them."

"Does he break his word or keep it?"

"He's one of those who swear they will."

I began to feel a little better. I recovered gradually as from a brutal and unexpected fall, and a salutary anger started replacing disappointment. We were separated by a wall of falseness. Her battle was still unfought, that was why she had come back.

"Odd that you don't want to identify. Aren't you tempted the least bit?" she said maliciously.

For the second time I felt that I could have killed her though I didn't know exactly why.

"You are deceiving yourself," I said. "It is yourself you are deceiving now. You are doing violence to your feelings. You went to him because you were longing for Kustaa Mauri. Didn't you? You couldn't stand being alone. I would have done the same if I had had legs to go on. And I would have come back in just as wretched a state, just as crushed, more unhappy than ever. So he still hasn't got in touch with you? That's the only thing all this tells me."

"Oh yes, he got in touch with me."

It was again my turn to be surprised.

"So . . . now I don't understand anything anymore."

"One can see that."

She tortured me heartlessly by a prolonged blowing of her nose and by thoroughly cleaning out both nostrils with her handkerchief twisted around her finger. Perhaps she had a sudden need for cleansing. She looked like a bird preening its feathers, pressed her stomach, rotated her head, and twisted her neck. They were, naturally, sore; it is in the shoulders and the intestines that one experiences everything.

I could not keep still. I had a violent longing to be able to walk back and forth across the room—what a relief it would have been. Finally I sat down in the chair opposite her and saw her wiping her face, rubbing it with her hands as was her habit.

"Did he telephone? Have you met?"

I almost screamed.

"Now I understand why I didn't come here. I can't stand this interrogation. He phoned."

"What did he say?"

"As far as I remember he asked whether one of the dogs' collar and leash had possibly got left in the country."

I asked for water again. She gave me the glass, in which there was still a drop in the bottom.

"And nothing else?" I said, swallowing it.

"Well, the sort of things you generally say on the phone. Like how are you, how nice it was last time, and of course it would be good to meet again sometime, but just now he was enormously busy."

"That pig, that vermin . . . Didn't you ask anything?"

"What could I have asked him? The only question I want to ask him is: 'Why did you reject me?' "

It was dusk and I could not from my chair see her face clearly. She sat bowed, her hands on her temples, her hair over her hands on both sides. It took some time before I realized that she was crying, that at some point she had started to cry.

I was lost, like a scientist suddenly let down by his own research. Language flew from my reach and the rock of linguistic psychology on which I had founded my whole life ("Everything is as it is best expressed") shook beneath me, vibrating my soul with a dangerous resonance.

Her crying had started from the mouth and her last words had to swim through her tears like a message in a bottle thrown into the sea at the last minute. As her sobbing increased it penetrated ever deeper layers, until the ultimate reaches of her soul capitulated before the basic question, the key one, the question she had not dared ask. But even that was not sufficient: she must accept the fact that there would never be an answer, and even if there were it would never be satisfactory.

She started to come toward me, but the attempt ended halfway; she threw herself on the floor and screamed there. Screaming is man's first and last right, as we had agreed at times, and I did not consider I could prevent it even in the name of sympathy and care. Scrupulous as I am about the furnishings of my room, I would at that moment have allowed her to throw up on the rug. I think I repeated the words "Tamara, Tamara." I think I cried too; the opening of the ducts had occurred in me also. I cannot say how long this lasted.

Finally she began to wail words.

At first I distinguished amid her screams only such fragmentary phrases as "This cannot be the purpose" and "What a fool I was to teach that wretch to make love," and "How can he be so immoral," and "I'll burn all those books about Doberman pinschers!"

Then the crying changed to showers of words, just as interjections, cries of pain, and sobbing became comprehensible language:

"If only I could have managed to reject him. That's how it is. The one who does the rejecting first is the winner. And that's what lovers use to protect themselves and inflict pain.

226

That's how he got me. Perhaps that is just what he wanted out of love—to be able to cause pain and disappointment. That's what impotence really is. He just couldn't do it with me physically. It's horrible."

Now I began to get my gift of speech back and words returned in flocks.

"Very true," I said, "love is a terrifying thing."

"But I'll never, never let him know it. I won't give him that pleasure. Or may tell him one day, when it doesn't mean anything to me anymore, if the opportunity comes. So that he can know that about people along with all he knows about dogs. Perhaps it will help him to find a woman who can free him from his mental impotence as I freed him physically. And I, like a fool, went consciously looking for a normal man instead of a neurotic in order to get security and continuity. But it's these normal ones that are the really treacherous ones. The neuroses of a neurotic never deceive."

"On the contrary," I started to console her, "on the contrary. Everything went according to plan, you actually made progress. Instead of a neurotic you found a psychopath, a person without any emotional life at all, the most unshaken type there can be."

"What happened to him physically with me may happen mentally with someone else."

I felt that this was the turning point of her suffering: she understood Kustaa Mauri as far as one can understand another in a matter of this kind, even a little further. I felt, practically saw, how her spirit expanded from this perception and took in obstacles before which she had previously stopped irresolute. After this the only necessary therapy would be harping on the subject to calm the soul in theory. As it was in fact:

"He came to me like you come to a masseur or a sauna."

"Well, and what is there to complain about that? They're both respected institutions."

"But you order them and if you change your mind you

227

politely cancel them. It's only people you can reject without saying anything, leave them like a rag in the corner, without a word of explanation. And still he said, at least that one time . . ."

A brighter tone penetrated her crying as if a slightly hoarse flute had in its gentleness overridden for a moment the thunder of the orchestra.

"My poor darling," I said, finding the most ordinary words possible. "So this is how barren he was, your love made him flower."

"I have a right to him. I have, I have, according to everything that is morally right," she repeated; and I took refuge in another well-worn but serviceable expression, so banal that I felt ashamed of it even in this emergency situation:

"Have you forgotten that you can never own another person, not even through love?"

"But I don't want to own him," she screamed. "This is a question of the right to use and enjoy. Women ought to come and thank me for training him as I did."

"True," I said, "so they ought. But what did I say about the young woodpeckers after they learn to fly, you remember the young woodpeckers, woody-woody-woodpecker . . ."

"Or he's simply stupid, an imbecile to let a woman like me slip from his hands. I was so good to him—I couldn't be better to anyone. The one who loses me is the loser. And he humiliated me so. And maybe only because those dogs couldn't stand me and I hated them with their perpetual sneering," she sobbed, not noticing the ridiculousness of what she said.

"Just think what a humiliating situation it must have been for him. You were crushingly superior. As a matter of fact the poor man has done nothing else than provide you with a little joy and a change, but you changed his life decisively. What could he have given you in return?"

"Continuity. And I'd have been satisfied with very little. The minimum. I'd have been prepared to say: 'I'll always love you whenever you give me the opportunity.' How can you blame me?"

"The laws of love are the cruellest in the world," I said solemnly. "And sometimes it really seems that you know nothing about them at all. One cannot do that to oneself. It will not succeed because your self-esteem will revolt at the first opportunity."

"But I'm superior to you too."

"No, you are not. I fly."

She cried so much that I was afraid she would lose consciousness. At that moment she felt that even I rejected her.

"Tamara," I said, "you will always suffer, you must accept that. That's where your strength is. You are healthy, you can afford to suffer. People will always cause you suffering. But they will always need you, even depend on you in all sorts of ways. It is only that your own conditions for love will never come true, because they do not exist. You are unconditional and life is conditionalized."

"If only there was someone or something that would help. I said to that long-pants man: 'Fuck me into a communist. Maybe politics will help. I can't stand this anymore. I'll turn everything upside down. I won't leave one stone on top of another.' And then I'm supposed to give advice to others!"

"You can stand it. Oh yes, you can stand it. You can stand anything. And you will always go to love with your arms wide open, even after this experience, that's where your strength lies. But you'll always be hurt. Don't be afraid of pain. You've taught me that yourself. Surely you don't want to become petrified even if you bump into blockheads. Better a broken heart than no heart at all."

She rose to come over to me, and as she rose, staggering to her feet, down her legs trickled the sperm that had been inside her all the time—apparently it sometimes stays there for quite a long time—and ran on the carpet; she was evidently not even wearing panties.

"Sorry," she said, not knowing how much more I was prepared to allow.

"That's all right. Really. That's only good."

I gave her my handkerchief and she rubbed at the spot with it and her hair, which always got mixed up in everything she did.

But she still could not manage to get as far as me; she stayed on the floor leaning against the end of the desk, near my legs.

"I've been controlling myself all these days—it's only now I'm able to complain," she said.

"Never mind. I'll look after you. I'll wash you. I'll bathe the sorrow away. I'll rinse you till you are my own, deodorize you into gaiety again, bit by bit. This is only an episode, after all, not even the first, and scarcely the last."

Again she started to come toward me, but at the same time the telephone rang and we were both startled. I don't think either of us realized for a moment what it was, we had been so much in another world. Then it rang again.

Tamara went to answer it.

"Yes," she said, and sat down on the floor beside the telephone table, leaning her head on the table and shutting her eyes.

"Yes, you certainly are disturbing me calling at this time— I'm tired, been up all night. But never mind. I understand. But you must understand too. Yes, I've been in the country. Well, I'm wearing a skirt this time and a brown blouse. I don't know why."

A pause while she considered for a moment. Then she said:

"Rose-pink."

Again a pause.

"They're rose-pink too. Yes, they're lace, rose-pink lace. With lilies and touch-me-nots."

She supported her head with her hand.

"Well, it's more or less the same color as before, just faded a bit from the sun. Yes, it's quite a tangle."

She put the receiver down beside her as if she no longer had the strength to hold it in her hand.

"I love you," I could hear a man's voice saying, "I kiss your lovely crack, I spread it open, I lick its folds, I drink your juice, you taste good, I have longed for you, and now I go into you, you surround me, I am in you, and now I begin to move, you are my . . ."

Tamara picked up the receiver again.

"I must ring off now. I don't feel well, I'm quite worn out."

"Don't finish just yet," came from the telephone, "give me a few more seconds, you're wonderful, I come into you, now I come, I come, I come. Now."

Tamara waited a moment longer.

"Keep well," she said then.

"Oh, thank you, thank you, God bless you," said the telephone as Tamara replaced the receiver.

There is continuity for you, I felt like saying, but no longer had the heart.

She remained leaning against the telephone table for a moment as if to gather her strength, then she moved beside me on the floor and finally laid her head in my lap. I pushed my fingers into her ruffled hair; how they had longed for each other, these dumb parts of the body.

"Perhaps he has started to be faithful now that he has a reason for it. Or perhaps he began to fear that he was caught," I said to lighten the atmosphere. But everything, this whole question, began at the same moment to seem indifferent to me, of secondary value, compared with the fact that Tamara was there, and that we were together, Tamara and I. That was the heart of the matter. And it seemed to me that she must feel it too.

"Are there any more theories?" I said, taking her face between my hands and turning it toward me.

"They're of no importance anymore," she said, "they're all

231

side issues. There's only one question. And that is: Why am I always rejected?"

Surprisingly she grasped me by the waist and shook me so hard that it hurt, my eyes smarted, and it was my turn to want to scream, my back felt as if a knife had been plunged into it.

"You too," she said. "You too. You deny me your body. A woman experiences that as rejection. Everywhere's full of people rejected in different ways, people of all ages, all sorts and conditions. Life is the history of rejections. There's no more important question in the world than this. Why does it seem so familiar? Why did you reject me? Where have I heard that before? Or is the question already there in us, a heritage of the blood?"

Something strange began to happen in me. My head sang. I was dizzy, but I felt light as if I was just about to fly. Something in me concentrated on preparing to rise. And it happened as in the dream that I had had in the country: Tamara began to shell me, to take away the armor that squeezed and pressed, to seek for me beneath it, and when she opened the last hatch of the capsule, the space rocket sprang into sight and stood there gigantic, ready to leave, almost exploding from its own power.

And Tamara rose on to my knees, placed it inside herself, and began to move slowly, her whole body trembling, her brow against my temples, salty.

And I felt myself being released into her space, leaving on the journey that I had dreamed of, toward the goal that mankind has striven for throughout its whole existence. And joined together we plunged past the moon, through star dust, beyond the quasars, toward the limits of existence.

But just when we were about to crash where everything ends, and I felt for the first time in my life that I was ready to die, she slowed down and said: "I want to be here a little longer."

Or did I only imagine? Like everything else.

232

THE AUTHOR

EEVA KILPI, born in 1928, is one of Finland's most distinguished writers. She grew up in Karelia, an area of Finland ceded to the Russians after World War II. She did not begin writing until she was thirty-one, and since then has published several novels, collections of short stories, and poetry. The sexual focus of *Tamara* created a great stir in Finland, which has no tradition of erotic literature. When asked why she chose to tell her story through the eyes of a paralyzed scholar, she explains: "The disability of the narrator is based on my notion that we are all emotionally injured; the world is so unkind to emotion that it either dies or becomes crippled, trodden like a weed between the pavement stones."

Since its publication in Finland in 1972, *Tamara* has appeared in Germany, Sweden, France, Holland, Yugoslavia, and Japan.